PATRIK IAN MEYER

THE **5 PILLARS** OF
BRAIN
OPTIMIZATION

77 TECHNIQUES &. HACKS

TO ACHIEVE PEAK PERFORMANCE WITH COGNITIVE FITNESS.

Get Extraordinary Results in Life Through Brain Training,
Smart Thinking, and Mental Sharpness

Table of Contents

Introduction

Diving into the world of brain optimization is like solving a captivating puzzle that unveils the secrets to unlocking our cognitive potential. This enthralling pursuit offers a new perspective on mental enhancement for those who desire to improve brain function and live a fulfilling life.

For those eager to rekindle their brain's vibrant capabilities and ensure its continued high-level functioning, brain optimization shines a guiding light. Though the journey may present challenges, overcoming these obstacles will reveal the true potential of your mind and empower you to live a life marked by cognitive excellence.

Our brain, the most precious gift we possess, governs every aspect of our lives. Its health and fitness are paramount, as it controls everything we do. Studies have demonstrated that we can retrain our brain to regain its former potential and prevent decline. This realization inspired me to delve deeper into the intricate workings of the brain, ultimately leading to the creation of this book, which shares my findings and passion for brain optimization.

This book aims to provide accessible information on brain optimization skills that have motivated individuals across various age groups to nurture their cognitive health and enhance their quality of life. As such, brain optimization can help overcome cognitive decline, regardless of age. By embracing this opportunity consistently, you can harness the power to change from within.

This book contains five pillars of brain optimization that can transform your understanding of how the mind functions as it ages. These pillars encompass diet, daily routines, decision-making, and socialization, all impacting your well-being. Likewise, discover the science behind these theories and receive practical strategies and advice to implement immediately and in the future. You will find 77 techniques, tips, and strategies on how to significantly influence brain health peppered throughout the entire book. It's intentionally designed this way to serve as your guide along each step of the process.

Taking a simple yet powerful approach to brain optimization, the first chapter delves into the brain's anatomy, structure, function, information processing, and capacity for retraining. Subsequent chapters detail the five major pillars that significantly influence brain health, equipping you with tools, strategies, and exercises to cultivate a flexible, potent, energized, and fit brain. The final chapter synthesizes this newfound knowledge and guides you on incorporating these lessons into your daily life.

This book is designed to make brain optimization accessible to anyone seeking to improve their cognitive health. By embracing the opportunity to grow your brain today and every day, you tap into the innate power to change and foster a thriving brain.

Chapter 1:
Brain Basics

As the body's most intricate organ, the brain expertly manages various processes such as cognition, motion, and sensation. Weighing merely three pounds, this remarkable organ within the skull consists of billions of neurons interacting via chemical and electrical signals. This chapter will delve into the brain's physiology, organization, information-processing capacities, memory, and learning. Exploration of these topics will enhance our comprehension of the brain's workings, empowering us to optimize its function and improve our overall well-being.

Anatomy

The human brain is an extraordinary masterpiece of complexity and intricacy, holding the key to unleashing our true potential. To truly optimize our brains, it is essential to grasp their remarkable anatomy. Deep within our skulls, a vast network of interconnected neurons forms an intricate communication system. Acting as tiny information processors, these neurons transmit signals and messages throughout the brain. Specialized regions organize these neurons, each contributing to our overall cognitive abilities.

One remarkable region is the **parietal lobe**, situated at the top and towards the back of the skull. It plays a crucial role in processing sensory information, including touch, temperature, and spatial awareness. By enabling us to perceive and navigate the world around us, the parietal lobe allows us to engage in complex tasks that require spatial orientation and coordination.

As we move to the front of the brain, we encounter the **frontal lobe**, often considered the control center of our cognitive functions. Responsible for higher-level thinking processes, such as decision-making, problem-solving, and logical reasoning, the frontal lobe houses the prefrontal cortex. This region governs our ability to plan, set goals, and exercise self-control, playing a pivotal role in our executive functions and enabling us to make sound judgments, regulate behavior, and adapt to new situations.

Towards the back of the brain lies the **occipital lobe**, responsible for processing visual information. This region allows us to perceive and interpret the world through sight, recognizing objects, shapes, colors, and faces. Likewise, it plays a vital role in visual memory, enabling us to store and recall visual information with precision.

Meanwhile, the **temporal lobe** is on the sides of the brain, near our ears. These lobes encompass critical structures in auditory processing, language comprehension, and memory formation. Through the temporal lobes, we perceive and interpret sounds, understand spoken language, and remember past experiences. They also house the hippocampus, a key structure in forming long-term memories.

Aside from that, at the brain's core lies the **cerebrum**. Divided into two hemispheres, left and right, each hemisphere carries out distinct cognitive functions. The **left hemisphere** governs logical thinking, language processing, and analytical abilities. Meanwhile, the **right hemisphere** thrives in creativity, spatial awareness, and holistic thinking. Working together, these hemispheres shape our thoughts, perceptions, and actions, combining their strengths harmoniously.

Understanding the intricate anatomy of our brains offers us a glimpse into their astounding wonders. Each region, structure, and connection uniquely shapes our thoughts, behaviors, and overall cognitive abilities.

Structure

As aforementioned, the brain's anatomy addresses its physical composition. Meanwhile, the structure delves into the organization and relationships among its components.

Central to the brain's structure is the **central nervous system**, which comprises the brain and spinal cord. The brain consists of distinct regions, each responsible for specific functions. Regions like the cerebral cortex, hippocampus, and cerebellum collaborate seamlessly, orchestrating our thoughts, memories, movements, and emotions.

Neurons, the specialized cells within the brain's structure, play a pivotal role. They transmit electrical signals and information, fostering communication and coordination among regions. Likewise, they form intricate networks called neural pathways, enabling efficient information transmission and processing.

Moreover, **glial cells**, often called the brain's "glue," provide essential support and nourishment, ensuring proper neuron function and overall brain health. Besides that, they regulate the brain's chemical environment, maintaining the necessary balance for optimal cognitive performance.

Various interconnected systems within the brain's structure, such as sensory systems, interpret information from our environment. Visual, auditory, and somatosensory systems harmonize to offer a comprehensive understanding of the world.

Furthermore, the brain's structure includes intricate connections between different regions, known as neural circuits. These circuits integrate information and facilitate complex processes like learning, memory formation, and decision-making. Harnessing the power of these neural circuits optimizes our brain's ability to process information efficiently and adaptively.

Function

The brain efficiently carries out numerous tasks by drawing upon the abilities of its diverse regions, such as:

Receive Sensory Input From the Environment

Our brain provides a gateway to the outside world, continuously receiving sensory inputs. Be it the warmth of sunlight, the aroma of the coffee, or a gentle touch, our brain processes these stimuli to create a rich tapestry of experiences. Sensations trigger a cascade of neural activity as receptors throughout our body send electrical signals to the brain. These signals transform into meaningful information, enabling us to perceive and interact with our surroundings.

Lead to Decision-Making, Goal-Setting, and Experiences

A symphony of neural activity within our brain orchestrates thoughts, emotions, and memories. Decisions are made, goals are set, and experiences are born. The prefrontal cortex, the brain's executive center, plays a crucial role in these cognitive processes. As such, it allows us to analyze information, weigh options, and make choices based on goals and values.

Allow Reasoning, Problem-Solving, and Cognitive Processes

As we encounter challenges, our brain engages in cognitive processes that involve analyzing, evaluating, and synthesizing information. These processes rely on various brain regions working harmoniously, exchanging signals and information through neural pathways. This capacity is essential for overcoming intellectual obstacles, adapting to new situations, learning from experience, and fostering personal growth.

Influence Thoughts, Beliefs, and Attitudes

Neuroscientists have discovered that specific brain regions underlie cognitive and emotional processes. For instance, the amygdala processes emotions, influences emotional responses, and shapes event perceptions. Brain plasticity allows thoughts, beliefs, and attitudes to evolve as neural connections adapt and reorganize. Understanding the brain's influence on our inner world offers insights into consciously shaping our thoughts, beliefs, and attitudes for more fulfilling lives.

Foster Learning, Skill Acquisition, and Recovery From Injuries

Neuroplasticity enables learning and skill acquisition throughout our lives. Engaging in learning activities, such as mastering a musical instrument, learning a language, or honing professional skills, leads to structural and functional brain changes. These changes reflect new neural connection formation and existing refinement, allowing performance improvement and ability expansion. Likewise, neuroplasticity is vital in recovering from strokes or traumatic brain injuries. Targeted rehabilitation and therapeutic interventions help the brain rewire, regain lost functions, and offer recovery possibilities.

Information Processing

Understanding how the brain processes information is paramount in our quest for brain optimization. With its intricate and awe-inspiring architecture, the brain serves as the ultimate information processing system, allowing us to make sense of the world around us and navigate life's complexities.

The first step in the brain's information processing begins with **gathering information** from our environment. Our senses capture this sensory input, such as the vibrant hues of a sunset, the delicate scent of a flower, or the melodic notes of a symphony. Each sense—sight, hearing, taste, smell, and touch—acts as a gateway, receiving and transmitting sensory information to the brain.

Once sensory input is captured, it **goes through the brain's intricate network of neurons.** These neurons form countless connections, creating a vast network of neural pathways. Likewise, they serve as highways for information transmission, allowing signals to travel swiftly and efficiently throughout the brain.

As sensory information traverses the neural pathways, the **brain takes center stage in perception and interpretation.** As such, sensory information integration allows us to recognize objects, understand language, and interpret the world around us.

Beyond perception and interpretation, the **brain engages in higher cognitive processes** that define our intellectual prowess. Thinking, reasoning, and problem-solving are among the cognitive abilities that rely on the brain's intricate workings. Memory formation and retrieval aid in storing and accessing information, allowing us to learn from the past and plan for the future. Meanwhile, attention and focus guide our ability to selectively process and attend to relevant information in a sea of stimuli.

Lastly, the brain's information processing culminates in the execution of motor responses. Translating the processed information into actions requires seamless coordination between the brain and muscles. The brain sends precise signals to the muscles, instructing them to do the desired movements.

Information Processing Model

Composed of three primary stages—*input, processing, and output*—the *"Information Processing Model"* provides a comprehensive framework for understanding how the brain processes and responds to information.

During the **input stage**, sensory perception and information gathering occur as our senses, such as sight, hearing, taste, smell, and touch, enable us to perceive our environment. The brain subsequently receives and processes this sensory input, converting it into meaningful information for further processing.

Meanwhile, the **processing stage** encompasses various cognitive processes. Attention enables selective focus on pertinent information while filtering distractions. Perception involves interpreting and organizing sensory information, allowing us to understand our surroundings. Then, memory is vital for storing and retrieving information, which lets us utilize past experiences and knowledge. Problem-solving and decision-making are cognitive processes that entail information analysis, solution generation, and selecting the optimal course of action.

In the **output stage**, the processed information is transformed into a response: physical actions, verbal responses, thoughts, or emotions. The brain integrates and coordinates these responses, facilitating our interaction with the world and effective self-expression.

Remarkably, the Information Processing Model bears similarities with computer functioning, as both systems involve input reception, information processing, and output production. The brain processes information like a computer, albeit with greater complexity and dynamism. Furthermore, the brain demonstrates exceptional adaptability and learning capabilities, comparable to computers being programmed and trained to enhance performance.

Comprehending the Information Processing Model and its parallels with computer functioning allows us to marvel at the human brain's incredible capabilities. Acknowledging the brain's adaptability and learning potential, we can proactively use strategies and exercises to optimize its function. This understanding enables us to boost our cognitive abilities, refine problem-solving and decision-making skills, and foster greater fulfilment and success in various life aspects. Ultimately, the Information Processing Model serves as a guide for unlocking our minds' full potential and leveraging the power of information processing to achieve personal growth and excellence.

Cognitive Belief System

In shaping our thoughts, emotions, and behaviors, the "Cognitive Belief System" represents a fundamental aspect of human cognition. As such, this system consists of interconnected components that influence our perception of the world and our navigation through life. Among these components, core beliefs hold significant importance. They are deeply ingrained convictions about ourselves, others, and the world, impacting how we interpret and make sense of our experiences. Acting as filters, they shape our thoughts, emotions, and behaviors through our worldview.

Additionally, the Cognitive Belief System encompasses automatic thoughts, which are immediate and spontaneous mental responses that arise in reaction to various situations. Either positive, negative, or neutral, these thoughts influence our emotional and behavioral responses. However, cognitive distortions can disrupt our thinking patterns within this belief system. These distortions involve biased and inaccurate ways of thinking that lead to cognitive errors. Examples include all-or-nothing thinking, overgeneralization, and mental filtering, distorting our perception of reality and affecting our overall well-being.

Furthermore, cognitive schemas act as mental frameworks that organize and interpret information. Moreover, various factors influence the formation and development of the Cognitive Belief System. Early childhood experiences, including the influence of family, caregivers, and the environment, shapes core beliefs and cognitive schemas. Social and cultural influences also contribute to forming our belief systems as we inherit societal and cultural norms, which shape our cognitive biases and automatic thoughts.

To challenge and restructure the Cognitive Belief System, various techniques and approaches can be employed. Cognitive restructuring techniques involve identifying and challenging cognitive distortions while replacing negative automatic thoughts with more realistic and positive ones. Additionally, cognitive-behavioral therapy (CBT) offers a therapeutic approach to address dysfunctional beliefs and thoughts, providing techniques to change cognitive patterns and improve overall well-being.

In everyday life, the Cognitive Belief System can be effectively applied through self-awareness and mindfulness. By recognizing and monitoring automatic thoughts and cognitive biases, individuals can better understand their belief systems and impact. Cultivating present-moment awareness enables individuals to observe their thoughts, emotions, and behaviors with greater clarity. Furthermore, cognitive strategies for problem-solving and decision-making enhance the Cognitive Belief System. Employing cognitive flexibility and critical thinking allows individuals to consider alternative perspectives and challenge assumptions, empowering them to make more informed and rational choices based on a broader understanding of their belief systems.

Memory

Serving as a complex mechanism, memory handles retaining and recalling information, experiences, and knowledge. This intricate network of connections interweaves each piece of information, forming a tapestry that defines our identity and shapes our understanding of the world.

Memory consists of three essential processes: *encoding, storage, and retrieval.* **Encoding** is the first stage, transforming incoming information into a format suitable for storage and processing within the brain, akin to creating a detailed blueprint. Following encoding, memories transition to **storage**, where they remain until needed. This extensive repository includes various memory types, each fulfilling a unique purpose. Meanwhile, short-term memory retains information briefly, such as recalling a phone number when dialing. Conversely, long-term memory preserves information over extended durations, from treasured childhood memories to skills developed over years of practice.

Retrieval, the final step, involves the brain accessing stored information and reintroducing it to our conscious awareness. This process resembles searching through a vast library and selecting the appropriate book. At times, retrieval is effortless, with memories seamlessly entering our thoughts; however, it occasionally demands more effort to uncover the desired recollection.

The remarkable feat of memory is achieved through the intricate collaboration of brain regions and neural networks. Regions such as the hippocampus and prefrontal cortex work together to encode, consolidate, and retrieve memories. Neurons communicate via complex electrical and chemical signals, establishing connections that underpin memory. Besides that, memory is a dynamic and adaptable process rather than a static entity. Factors, including emotions, attention, and external cues, can influence our memories. This adaptability enables us to modify and update our memories based on new experiences and information, continually refining our worldview.

Types

Three primary types of memory play distinct roles in our cognitive processes: *working memory, sensory memory, and short-term memory.*

Working memory is like the mental workspace of our brain. For instance, it refers to temporarily holding and manipulating information in our minds while performing cognitive tasks. Think of it as a whiteboard where we jot down and control thoughts, ideas, and calculations in real time. Likewise, this memory allows us to manipulate information mentally, keeping relevant details accessible while discarding unnecessary ones. Expanding the capacity and efficiency of our working memory enhances our cognitive abilities.

Meanwhile, **sensory memory** is the gateway through which our brain initially perceives the world around us. It acts as a temporary buffer, holding raw sensory information shortly before it either fades away or gets transferred to other memory systems. Imagine it as the first impression our brain forms when exposed to stimuli. Sensory memory is divided into different modalities: iconic memory (visual sensory memory) and echoic memory (auditory sensory memory). Honing our sensory memory sharpens our attention, perception, and ability to process sensory information swiftly and accurately.

Subsequently, **short-term memory**, also known as working memory's close cousin, refers to our brain's ability to hold and manipulate information for a brief duration. Unlike working memory, which focuses on active mental processing, short-term memory serves as a temporary storage space for information. As such, it enables us to retain and work with recently acquired knowledge or recall details needed for immediate tasks. For example, retaining a sentence while actively engaging in a conversation. Strengthening our short-term memory can improve focus, concentration, and the seamless flow of information between different cognitive processes.

These memory types work harmoniously, facilitating our perception, learning, and everyday cognitive functions. Understanding their unique roles and training them effectively empowers us to expand our mental capacities, improve information processing, and achieve greater cognitive performance.

Neuroplasticity

Neuroplasticity, a cornerstone of brain science, highlights the extraordinary adaptability of the human brain. Likewise, it refers to the brain's remarkable capacity for reorganization and adaptation in response to experiences, learning, and environmental changes. Contrary to the once-held belief that the brain's structure and functions were fixed, neuroplasticity demonstrates that it is highly dynamic and capable of rewiring itself throughout life. This reorganization allows the brain to adjust to new circumstances, acquire new skills, recover from injuries, and compensate for damage.

Moreover, neuroplasticity occurs throughout the lifespan, from early development to aging, although the extent and efficiency may differ. During early development, the brain exhibits exceptional plasticity, rapidly forming neural connections and refining its circuitry based on experiences and environmental interactions. In adulthood, neuroplasticity remains crucial for ongoing learning, memory consolidation, and skill acquisition. Even in older age, the brain retains the potential for plasticity, though the rate and effectiveness of adaptation may change.

Recognizing neuroplasticity throughout the lifespan offers valuable insights into the brain's capacity for growth, learning, and resilience.

Mechanisms of Neuroplasticity

Operating through several mechanisms, including *synaptic plasticity, structural plasticity, and functional plasticity*, neuroplasticity allows the brain to adapt and reorganize its structure and functions. As such, **synaptic plasticity** involves the strengthening or weakening of synapses, the connections between neurons. Repeated activation or stimulation can enhance communication and efficiency between neurons. Conversely, infrequently used synaptic connections may weaken or disappear. This fine-tuning of neural networks optimizes information transmission and facilitates learning and memory processes.

Structural plasticity encompasses the physical changes in the brain's structure in response to experiences and environmental influences. These modifications include alterations in neuron shape, size, connectivity, and new neuronal connections. Structural changes can result from neurogenesis or the remodeling of existing neural networks. These alterations shape the brain's architecture and circuitry, enabling adaptation to new situations and facilitating learning and memory processes.

Subsequently, **functional plasticity** refers to the reorganization of brain functions due to changes or damage in specific regions. When an area is compromised by injury or disease, other regions can compensate by assuming the affected area's functions. This adaptive reshuffling allows the brain to maintain essential functions and adapt to changing demands imposed by altered circumstances. Functional plasticity is also particularly evident during neurorehabilitation, where the brain can rewire itself to regain lost functions and restore cognitive abilities.

Examining the mechanisms of neuroplasticity, including synaptic, structural, and functional plasticity, offers insights into the brain's capacity for adaptation and growth. These mechanisms underscore the brain's remarkable flexibility and resilience, empowering individuals to harness the power of neuroplasticity for personal development.

Neuroplasticity and Learning

The brain's remarkable ability to reorganize and adapt allows for forming and strengthening neural connections. When learning, neuroplasticity enables the brain to reshape its neural pathways to accommodate and optimize the acquisition of knowledge and skills. As we engage in repetitive and focused practice, the connections between relevant neurons become more robust, facilitating efficient information processing and skill acquisition.

To optimize neuroplasticity during the learning process, certain strategies can be employed. One effective approach is to introduce variety and challenge into the learning experience. Exposing the brain to new and novel stimuli forces it to adapt and create new connections. As such, incorporate different learning techniques, use diverse resources, and engage in multidimensional activities. Additionally, maintaining an environment that fosters curiosity and active engagement promotes neuroplasticity. Actively participating in the learning process, asking questions, and seeking deeper understanding stimulate the brain's adaptive capacities, facilitating enhanced learning and retention.

Furthermore, the impact of motivation and engagement on neuroplasticity cannot be overstated. When individuals are intrinsically motivated and genuinely interested in the subject matter. Positive emotions associated with curiosity, excitement, and passion activate various brain regions involved in learning and memory, enhancing neural plasticity.

The brain's receptivity to new information and ability to establish and strengthen connections are amplified when individuals are fully engaged and motivated to learn.

Neuroplasticity and Mental Health

There is a strong connection between neuroplasticity and mental well-being. Neuroplasticity allows the brain to adapt and reorganize in response to experiences, thoughts, and emotions. Individuals can enhance their mental well-being and resilience by engaging in activities and interventions that promote neuroplasticity.

Harnessing neuroplasticity can be particularly beneficial in managing stress, anxiety, and depression. Chronic stress and mental health disorders can lead to negative brain structure and function changes. However, through interventions that stimulate neuroplasticity, individuals can reverse these changes and restore balance in the brain.

Cultivating Neuroplasticity in Everyday Life

Actively shaping our brain's structure and function enhances cognitive abilities and overall well-being. Several essential factors and strategies support the cultivation of neuroplasticity in daily life.

- **Lifestyle factors** like sleep and nutrition are crucial in maintaining neuroplasticity. Quality sleep consolidates memories and strengthens neural connections, while a balanced diet provides the necessary nutrients and energy for optimal brain function.

- **Enriching environments** foster neuroplasticity by stimulating diverse experiences and intellectually challenging activities that encourage new neural connections.

• **Embracing novelty, challenges, and lifelong learning** promotes neuroplasticity by pushing the brain to develop new strategies and neural networks and refine existing connections.

To harness neuroplasticity's power, various strategies and practices can be incorporated into daily routines:

 • **Brain exercises and cognitive training** stimulate the brain, encouraging the formation of new connections and improving cognitive performance.

 • **Environmental enrichment** includes exposure to sensory experiences and intellectually engaging surroundings that impact brain adaptability.

 • **Mindfulness and meditation practices** strengthen attention, emotion regulation, and self-awareness, resulting in structural and functional changes in the brain.

 • **Physical exercise** boosts blood flow, improves mood, enhances cognitive function, and supports the growth and survival of new neurons, contributing to neuroplasticity.

Incorporating these strategies and practices into daily routines enables us to tap into neuroplasticity's incredible power and actively shape our brain's capacity for learning, adaptation, and growth. Cultivating neuroplasticity empowers us to unlock our brain's potential and lead a fulfilling, intellectually vibrant existence.

Brain Development

The brain undergoes remarkable transformations from infancy to adulthood, shaping our cognitive abilities, emotions, and overall functioning. Understanding this process of brain development aids in optimizing the brain's potential.

Prenatal Brain Development

Brain optimization begins long before we take our first breath. From the moment of conception, an intricate process unfolds within the womb. The developing brain undergoes extraordinary transformations, shaping the blueprint for our future neural networks. For instance, it is a symphony of genetic instructions, cellular proliferation, and intricate connections.

As the weeks and months pass, the prenatal brain rapidly evolves. Neurogenesis, the formation of new neurons, occurs at a staggering rate. Billions of neurons are generated, each seeking its place within the vast network of the brain. This process sets the stage for the remarkable complexity that our brains possess.

Simultaneously, neural migration takes place. Newly formed neurons embark on a mesmerizing journey, traveling to their designated locations within the brain. Guided by chemical cues and intricate signaling pathways, they navigate paths, ensuring precise placement and connectivity.

During this period, the brain is susceptible to environmental influences. Experiences, both positive and negative, can leave lasting imprints on the developing neural architecture. A nurturing and supportive environment can foster optimal brain growth, while adverse conditions can disrupt this delicate process.

The prenatal brain is not merely a passive recipient of stimuli. In fact, it is an active participant in its development. Neural connections are refined through a process known as synaptic pruning, where weaker connections are eliminated and stronger connections are reinforced. This sculpting process continues throughout childhood and adolescence, shaping the neural circuitry that underlies our cognitive abilities.

Early Childhood Development

In early childhood, our brains experience rapid growth and development, forming neural connections that are the groundwork for future learning and cognitive functioning. This immense potential and sensitivity phase allows experiences and interactions to impact brain development profoundly.

Children's brains exhibit extraordinary plasticity in their early years, enabling them to absorb information and acquire skills at an incredible rate. Each interaction, spoken word, and encountered experience contributes to the intricate wiring of their brains. Through these experiences, neural pathways are strengthened, establishing the foundation for future cognitive abilities, emotional well-being, and social skills.

The brain's capacity for learning and adaptation peaks during early childhood, characterized by rapid language development, motor skill acquisition, and social connection formation. With the brain eagerly absorbing information, it presents an opportune moment for enriching experiences and stimulating environments. Providing a nurturing and engaging environment optimizes brain development and unlocks its full potential.

Furthermore, early childhood experiences leave a lasting impact on brain architecture. Positive and supportive interactions with caregivers, exposure to rich language, and participation in stimulating activities all contribute to the growth of neural networks. These experiences shape the brain's structure, enhancing its capacity for learning, memory, and problem-solving.

On the other hand, adverse experiences during early childhood can negatively affect brain development. Stressful environments, neglect, or exposure to trauma can hinder neural growth and disrupt healthy brain functioning. Recognizing the importance of early childhood development empowers us to create nurturing environments and provide supportive experiences that promote optimal brain growth and well-being.

Adolescent Brain Development

The teenage years signify a crucial phase in brain development, characterized by substantial remodeling and reorganization of neural circuits. This period, known as adolescent brain development, presents opportunities and challenges.

An integral aspect of adolescent brain development is synaptic pruning, where infrequently used or strengthened connections are eliminated to optimize neural efficiency. This process refines the brain's networks and enhances its capacity for specialized functions. Subsequently, during adolescence, the prefrontal cortex, responsible for executive processes such as decision-making and impulse control, undergoes significant maturation. For instance, this development increases our capacity for abstract thought and long-term planning. However, the delayed maturation of the prefrontal cortex can also explain the heightened risk-taking tendencies and emotional reactivity often associated with adolescence.

The intricate interplay between hormonal changes, environmental factors, and adolescent brain development profoundly impacts mental health and well-being. Conditions like depression, anxiety, and substance use disorders often emerge or intensify during this developmental stage, emphasizing the importance of providing support and resources to adolescents during this crucial period. Recognizing the changes and challenges of adolescent brain development can help inform interventions and strategies that promote positive outcomes.

Pillar 1:
Nutrition

Optimizing brain function requires a strong emphasis on good nutrition. This section explores the profound impact that nutrition has on the brain. As such, the brain is an incredibly metabolically active organ, constantly consuming energy and requiring a continuous supply of nutrients to function optimally. Understanding the relationship between nutrition and the brain leads to harnessing good nutrition's power to enhance mood, memory, and cognitive function.

This pillar emphasizes the importance of providing the brain with the right nutrients. For instance, it explores the specific role of key nutrients, including carbohydrates, proteins, lipids, vitamins, and minerals, in supporting brain health. These nutrients are essential in the brain's structure, functioning, and cell communication. A well-balanced intake of these nutrients can fuel the brain and promote optimal performance.

In addition to understanding the essential nutrients for brain health, this pillar emphasizes the significance of a healthy diet. A diet rich in fruits, vegetables, whole grains, and lean meats provides the necessary nutrients to sustain top brain performance. On the other hand, a diet high in sugar, processed foods, and saturated fats can impair brain function and contribute to cognitive decline.

Under nutrition, the concept of *"brain superfoods"* is explored. These foods have been scientifically shown to enhance brain function and support cognitive health. Examples of brain superfoods include blueberries, which are rich in antioxidants that protect brain cells. Aside from that are almonds, which provide essential fatty acids for brain health.

Lastly, this pillar highlights the benefits of specific eating habits linked to better cognitive performance and reduced risk of cognitive decline. Likewise, it delves into the importance of regular meals, balanced daily nutrition, and mindful eating practices. Adopting these habits can optimize our brain function and support long-term brain health.

Chapter 2:
Brain Food

In the extensive domain of nourishment, where taste and sustenance harmoniously coexist, a unique category known as *"brain food"* emerges. These edible wonders hold a secret power to unlock the hidden potential within our minds, weaving a symphony of flavors that stimulate neurons and ignite thoughts.

How Nutrition and Diet Affect Brain Health

Nutrition sustains optimal brain health, as the brain relies on a constant supply of essential nutrients to function effectively. However, nutrient deficiencies can have far-reaching consequences, affecting brain health and performance.

Cognitive decline is one of the most notable effects of nutrient deficiencies, with research indicating that insufficient intake of key nutrients can impair memory, attention, and overall cognitive abilities. These deficiencies can result in concentration difficulties, decreased mental agility, and issues with learning and problem-solving. Nonetheless, a well-balanced diet helps maintain our brain's cognitive functions, allowing us to perform optimally in daily tasks and activities.

Moreover, nutrient deficiencies can elevate the **risk of neurodegenerative diseases**, including Alzheimer's and Parkinson's. Scientific studies have established a connection between poor nutrition and these debilitating conditions. Therefore, a nutrient-rich diet is essential for present brain health and for reducing future neurodegenerative disease risks.

Additionally, nutrient deficiencies **impact children's brain development** during critical growth stages. Proper nutrition is crucial during these periods, as inadequate nutrient intake can hinder neural connections and potentially cause long-term cognitive and learning consequences. Ensuring sufficient nutrition during early life supports optimal brain development and lays the foundation for future cognitive abilities and academic success.

Mediterranean Diet and Brain Health

Renowned for its numerous health benefits, the Mediterranean diet has become a powerful way to enhance cognitive function. Drawing inspiration from the traditional diets of Mediterranean countries, this eating pattern brims with fresh fruits and vegetables, whole grains, legumes, nuts, seeds, and olive oil. Scientific investigations have illuminated the multifaceted ways in which adopting a Mediterranean diet can elevate cognitive function. Abounding in antioxidants and anti-inflammatory compounds, this dietary regimen shields brain cells from oxidative stress and inflammation, fostering improved cognitive performance. Additionally, incorporating wholesome fats like omega-3 fatty acids from fish and monounsaturated fats from olive oil nurtures brain health and potentially curtails the risk of cognitive decline and neurodegenerative ailments.

Scientific research further underscores the potential of adhering to a Mediterranean diet to diminish the likelihood of developing Alzheimer's disease, an insidious neurodegenerative condition. The amalgamation of nutrient-rich foods within this diet, alongside its encouragement of moderate alcohol consumption and engagement in social activities, confers a protective shield upon brain health. An elevated intake of fruits, vegetables, whole grains, and fish, alongside the restriction of red meat and processed foods, has exhibited a correlation with a reduced incidence of Alzheimer's disease. Embracing the Mediterranean diet offers individuals a means to promote their brain health, potentially reducing the risk of cognitive decline and dementia.

High-Sugar and Processed Food Diet

Contrariwise, diets with high-sugar and processed foods take a toll on cognitive abilities. Overindulgence in sugar, particularly through sugary beverages and heavily processed foods, impairs cognitive function. Consuming copious amounts of added sugars has been linked to diminished memory, attention, and learning capabilities. This deleterious impact of sugar on the brain stems from its propensity to incite inflammation, oxidative stress, and insulin resistance, all of which undermine brain health.

Furthermore, mounting evidence posits a plausible connection between an unhealthy diet and mental health disorders. Studies have discerned that diets teeming with processed foods, saturated fats, and added sugars contribute to an augmented vulnerability to depression, anxiety, and other mood disorders. Though the precise mechanisms behind this association continue to be explored, it is widely believed that disruptions in the gut-brain axis and the chronic inflammation ensuing from poor dietary choices influence mental health outcomes.

Discerning the divergent effects of distinct dietary patterns empower us to make informed choices that optimize brain health. Embracing the Mediterranean-style eating pattern, replete with nutrient-dense whole foods, furnishes the brain with the indispensable nutrients and protective compounds indispensable for supporting cognitive function and curbing the risk of neurodegenerative diseases. Conversely, curtailing the consumption of high-sugar and processed foods acts as a bulwark for cognitive abilities while cultivating mental well-being. Our dietary choices have an instrumental role in optimizing brain health, and by nurturing our bodies with wholesome foods, we unlock the boundless potential of our minds.

Nutrients Needed by the Brain

The human brain, a highly intricate organ, relies on various nutrients to function effectively. These essential nutrients contribute to brain growth and function while safeguarding the brain against damage from various environmental factors. Some of the nutrients that the brain needs include:

Omega-3 Fatty Acids

Renowned for their remarkable impact on brain function, omega-3 fatty acids maintain brain cells' structural integrity and facilitate communication. Furthermore, they promote healthy cognitive processes such as memory, focus, and mood regulation. Fatty fish like salmon and sardines, walnuts, and flaxseeds are excellent omega-3 sources that can help nourish our brains and support optimal cognitive function.

Antioxidants

The brain's vulnerability to oxidative stress can result in cellular damage and age-related cognitive decline. Antioxidants, functioning as the brain's natural defense system, neutralize harmful free radicals and protect brain cells from oxidative damage. Including antioxidant-rich foods in our diets strengthens the brain's defense mechanisms and fosters long-term brain health. Antioxidant powerhouses include berries *(blueberries and strawberries)*, dark chocolate, and leafy greens like spinach.

B Vitamins

Supporting cognitive function and maintaining optimal brain health are essential roles of B vitamins. For instance, B vitamins are part of various brain processes, including energy production, neurotransmitter synthesis, and DNA repair, contributing to mental clarity, focus, and overall cognitive performance.

Whole grains like brown rice and quinoa serve as excellent B vitamin sources, providing complex carbohydrates that steadily release energy while supplying the brain with crucial nutrients. Additionally, leafy greens such as spinach and kale are abundant in B vitamins, particularly folate, which plays a vital role in brain development and mood regulation. Incorporating these nutrient-dense vegetables into your diet can nourish your brain and promote optimal functioning.

Legumes, including lentils and chickpeas, offer another fantastic source of B vitamins. These plant-based protein sources provide sustainable energy and an array of vitamins essential for brain health. Including legumes in your meals can enhance your brain's nutrient intake and boost cognitive performance.

Vitamin D

Significantly contributing to brain development and function, vitamin D is also essential for maintaining bone health. Maintaining adequate vitamin D levels can lead to improved cognitive performance, mood regulation, and a reduced risk of neurodegenerative diseases.

Sunlight serves as a natural source of vitamin D, but certain foods can also supply this crucial nutrient. Fatty fish like salmon and mackerel, rich in omega-3 fatty acids, are excellent dietary sources of vitamin D, supporting brain health while reducing inflammation and enhancing neural communication. Fortified dairy products such as milk and yogurt also provide valuable sources of vitamin D, ensuring that individuals with dietary restrictions can maintain optimal levels for their brain's health and function.

Magnesium

In promoting neural transmission and synaptic plasticity, magnesium is a mineral that holds a pivotal role. As such, it is involved in hundreds of biochemical reactions within the brain, contributing to memory formation, learning, and overall cognitive function. Maintaining sufficient levels of magnesium can support a healthy brain and enhance mental performance.

Nuts, such as almonds and cashews, are excellent sources of magnesium. Incorporating these nutrient-dense snacks into your diet can provide a natural and convenient way to boost your brain's magnesium levels. Seeds, including pumpkin seeds and sunflower seeds, are another great option, offering a concentrated dose of magnesium along with other beneficial nutrients. Additionally, leafy greens like spinach and Swiss chard contain magnesium, making them an essential part of a brain-optimizing diet. By including these magnesium-rich foods in your meals and snacks, you can nourish your brain and support its optimal functioning.

Iron

Iron is essential for optimizing brain function, as it aids in oxygen transport and supports cognitive processes. Being a vital component of hemoglobin, iron ensures efficient oxygen delivery to the brain and other crucial organs. Insufficient iron supply may result in the brain not receiving adequate oxygen, leading to symptoms like fatigue, poor concentration, and reduced cognitive performance.

Incorporating iron into your diet can be achieved through various dietary sources. Lean meats such as beef and poultry are excellent sources of heme iron, which the body absorbs more readily. Legumes like lentils and chickpeas provide non-heme iron for those following plant-based or vegetarian diets. Furthermore, dark leafy greens like spinach and kale offer nutrient-rich, iron-packed meal additions. Thus, these iron-rich foods promote optimal oxygen transport and cognitive function, enhancing your brain's overall performance. _To the brain for_

Zinc

As a vital mineral, zinc contributes to neurotransmitter function and memory formation, making it essential for brain optimization. This micronutrient facilitates communication between neurons in the brain, enabling efficient signal transmission crucial for cognitive processes, learning, and memory. Additionally, zinc regulates synaptic plasticity, which allows the brain to adapt and form new connections.

neuroplasticity

To maintain adequate zinc intake, incorporate zinc-rich foods into your diet. Seafood, such as oysters, crab, and lobster, are excellent sources of zinc. Lean meats like beef, poultry, and pumpkin seeds also provide this essential mineral. Including these zinc-rich foods in your diet can bolster neurotransmitter function, improve memory formation, and enhance your brain's performance.

Choline

As a precursor to acetylcholine, a neurotransmitter involved in memory and cognitive function, choline is essential for efficient communication between brain cells. Choline also contributes to forming and maintaining the brain's cell membranes, supporting overall brain health.

Besides that, eggs, known for being an excellent source of choline, can be a valuable addition to your meals. Then, the liver, either from chicken, beef, or other animals, is also a notable source of choline. Additionally, soybeans and soy products, such as tofu and edamame, provide a plant-based option to incorporate choline into your diet. Having choline-rich foods in your meals support optimal brain development, neurotransmitter synthesis, and cognitive function.

Food Recipes for Better Brain Power

Discover the captivating world of culinary delights, where flavors intertwine and ingredients harmonize to unlock the hidden powers of our brains. Envision a symphony of vibrant colors, tempting aromas, and tastes that awaken the senses, all carefully crafted to nourish your mind and fuel your focus. These exceptional recipes can help enhance cognitive prowess and infuse clarity into every thought.

Almond Orange Salmon

Savor the delightful blend of flavors and brain-enhancing nutrients with the Almond Orange Salmon recipe. Combining the nutritional strength of salmon with the wholesome goodness of almonds supplies your brain with a double dose of omega-3 fatty acids—an essential nutrient celebrated for its positive impact on cognitive function.

This recipe uses a low-heat cooking method to achieve tender, perfectly cooked salmon with a silky texture.

Ingredients

- 4 salmon fillets
- Zest and juice of an orange
- ⅔ cup chopped almonds
- 1 tablespoon of finely chopped flat-leaf parsley
- Olive oil
- Salt and pepper

Preparation

1. Allow the salmon fillets to reach room temperature by leaving them out for about 30 minutes.
2. Preheat the oven to 275°F (135°C) and position a baking rack in a sheet pan.
3. Mix the orange zest and juice, chopped almonds and parsley, ½ teaspoon salt, and ½ teaspoon pepper in a small bowl. Set aside.
4. Place the salmon fillets skin side down on the baking rack.

5. Drizzle approximately one teaspoon of olive oil over each fillet, then season with salt and pepper. Cook the salmon in the pre-heated oven for 20 minutes.

6. Gently press the almond mixture onto the salmon, ensuring an ample coating. Return the pan to the oven for five minutes, allowing the almonds to toast beautifully.

The salmon will be cooked through, displaying a vibrant color and a delicate texture.

Blueberry-Banana Smoothie

Brimming with nutrient-dense ingredients, this smoothie is tasty and an excellent choice for boosting cognitive function.

Ingredients

- 1 cup milk
- ½ cup of frozen blueberries
- 1 ripe banana
- 4 to 5 ice cubes
- 1 tablespoon coconut oil
- 2 teaspoons flaxseed oil

Preparation

1. Combine the milk, frozen blueberries, ripe banana, coconut oil, and flaxseed oil in a blender.

2. Add ice cubes to the mixture.

3. Blend all ingredients until a smooth consistency is achieved.

4. Pour the smoothie into a glass.

Integrating this Blueberry-Banana Smoothie into your routine allows you to tap into the antioxidant power of blueberries, the healthy fats from coconut and flaxseed oil, and the natural sweetness and potassium of the banana.

Espresso Brownie Cake

Owing to the distinctive blend of meticulously chosen ingredients in Espresso Brownie Cake, it has the potential to boost cognitive function. For instance, espresso contains significant caffeine, a natural stimulant that improves alertness, focus, and concentration. Additionally, the rich dark chocolate used in the recipe is a source of flavonoids, an antioxidant linked to improved memory and cognitive performance.

Moreover, nuts and seeds can be incorporated into the brownie cake for a crunch and to boost brain power. These nutrient-dense ingredients are packed with healthy fats, vitamins, and minerals essential for optimal brain function. Together, these components create a dessert that satisfies your taste buds and supports your mental acuity.

Ingredients

- 1 cup of all-purpose flour
- 1 cup of sugar
- ½ cup of unsalted butter
- ½ teaspoon of baking soda
- ½ cup of coffee
- 3 tablespoons of unsweetened cocoa powder
- ¼ cup of buttermilk
- 1 egg

- 1 teaspoon of pure vanilla extract
- 1 teaspoon of aromatic cinnamon, supplying depth and warmth
- 1 cup of finely chopped dark chocolate

Preparation

1. Preheat your oven to 400°F.
2. Grease an 8 or 9-inch square pan with nonstick cooking spray and set aside.
3. Combine the all-purpose flour and sugar in a mixing bowl, creating the base for our scrumptious brownie cake.
4. Melt the unsalted butter, strong coffee, and unsweetened organic cocoa powder in a saucepan, allowing the flavors to blend and intensify.
5. Gently boil the mixture while stirring continuously for a smooth, velvety consistency.
6. Pour the rich cocoa mixture into the flour and sugar, integrating them into a uniform blend.
7. Mix until well combined, making sure no dry ingredients are left.
8. Incorporate the buttermilk, egg, baking soda, pure vanilla extract, and aromatic cinnamon into the mixture.
9. Stir in the finely chopped dark chocolate pieces.
10. Evenly distribute the batter into the prepared pan, ensuring consistent baking.
11. Place the pan in the preheated oven and bake for approximately 20 to 25 minutes, or until a toothpick inserted into the center comes out with a few moist crumbs attached.

12. Once perfectly baked, remove the Espresso Brownie Cake from the oven and let it cool.

Overall, this Espresso Brownie Cake not only pleases your palate but also offers numerous benefits to enhance brain power.

Tips for a Brain-Healthy Diet

Optimizing brain function and unlocking potential cognitive hinges on proper nutrition. Providing your body with essential nutrients enhances memory, focus, and brain health.

Begin **by incorporating brain-boosting foods** like colorful fruits and vegetables, rich in antioxidants and vital vitamins that protect brain cells from damage. **Include omega-3 fatty acids** by eating fatty fish such as salmon, trout, or sardines to support brain cell communication and improve cognitive function. Add nuts and seeds, like walnuts, almonds, and flaxseeds, which offer antioxidants and omega-3s, while opting for whole grains like quinoa, brown rice, and oats to provide steady energy release throughout the day.

Likewise, **maintain proper hydration** by drinking adequate water daily, as dehydration can impair cognitive function, concentration, and memory retention. Besides that, limit processed foods and added sugars, which contain unhealthy fats, sugars, and artificial additives that negatively impact brain health and cognitive abilities. Instead, reduce sugar intake and choose healthier alternatives.

Lastly, **practice portion control and mindful eating** to maintain a healthy weight, as obesity can increase cognitive decline risk. Savor meals by focusing on flavors, textures, and sensations, promoting healthy digestion and nutrient absorption through mindfulness.

A brain-healthy diet requires long-term commitment, but incorporating these tips into your lifestyle can lay the groundwork for optimal cognitive function. Experience improved focus, memory, and mental clarity as you embark on this journey toward brain optimization.

Pillar 2: Exercise

Often, many overlook the significant connection between our physical bodies and cognitive abilities. *Exercise is not just about toning muscles or fitting into our favorite jeans; it is a key factor in unlocking our brain's untapped potential.*

For instance, exercise enhances brain function by increasing blood flow, delivering essential nutrients and oxygen to brain cells. Additionally, it stimulates hormone production and growth factors that contribute to new brain cell creation and strengthen connections between existing cells. The cognitive benefits of regular exercise include improved memory, heightened attention, and enhanced executive function.

That said, this pillar explores various forms of exercise beneficial for the brain, such as aerobic and resistance training. Likewise, it talks about mind-body activities like yoga and tai chi, including practical tips for incorporating exercise into daily routines, regardless of schedule constraints or limited fitness facility access.

Following the recommendations in this pillar enhance your brain's health and function, ultimately improving your overall quality of life. Embrace exercise as a catalyst for unlocking cognitive potential and experiencing life with renewed vigor. Embark on this empowering journey to transform your brain and witness exercise's incredible impact on your world.

Chapter 3:
Physical Drills and Movement

In the pursuit of brain optimization, physical drills and movements act as dynamic partners, driving us toward cognitive excellence. These activities create a harmonious engagement between our bodies and minds, forming a deep connection that transcends traditional exercise boundaries. Envision the exhilaration of an exuberant dance or the adrenaline surge during an exciting game; moments when our spirits elevate, and our brains spark with electric potential. Thus, physical drills and movements energize our muscles and amplify our cognitive abilities as we participate in each step, jump, and stretch.

How Physical Activities Affect Brain Health

Physical activity is well-known for its importance in well-being, but its impact goes beyond physical fitness. Recent research reveals the significant influence of physical activities on brain health. The human brain, an intricate and extraordinary organ, flourishes with the stimulation of regular exercise. Some other influences of exercise on the brain include:

Enhancing Brain Function

Central to brain optimization is the concept of neuroplasticity. Contrary to previous beliefs that the brain's structure and abilities were fixed, neuroplasticity unveils the brain's impressive capacity to adapt and evolve throughout life. Our brains can form new neural connections, reorganize existing ones, and optimize functionality through neuroplasticity. Physical exercise is a potent catalyst for enhancing neuroplasticity by stimulating growth factor release and fostering new neuron and synapse creation. As such, regular physical activities unlock our potential to refine cognitive abilities like memory, attention, and learning, resulting in a more agile and resilient mind.

Defense Against Cognitive Decline

With age, the risk of cognitive decline and neurodegenerative diseases become increasingly relevant. However, physical activities can serve as a powerful defense against such conditions. Regular exercise reduces the risk of neurodegenerative diseases and preserves cognitive function. Likewise, physical activities protect the brain in several ways, including reducing inflammation, promoting healthy blood flow, and increasing antioxidant production, which shields brain cells from damage and supports their longevity.

Release of Endorphins and Their Mood-Boosting Effects

When exercising, our bodies release endorphins, often called the *"feel-good"* hormones. These endorphins act as natural painkillers and mood enhancers, instantly lifting our spirits and creating a sense of euphoria. The release of endorphins during exercise can immediately boost our overall mood and outlook on life.

Reduction of Stress, Anxiety, and Depression

Exercise serves as a powerful antidote to the pressures and challenges of daily life, effectively reducing stress, anxiety, and depression. During physical activity, our bodies release stress-busting hormones, such as cortisol and adrenaline, which help us manage and alleviate the negative effects of stress. Regular exercise acts as a natural stress reliever, promoting a sense of calm and tranquility. Moreover, it can significantly reduce symptoms of anxiety and depression by increasing the production of neurotransmitters like serotonin and dopamine, which regulate mood and promote feelings of happiness and contentment.

Improvement in Resilience to Stress and Sleep Quality

Engaging in regular physical activity not only reduces stress but also enhances our resilience to it. Challenging ourselves physically strengthens our bodies, making them more resilient to the adverse effects of stress. Besides that, exercise helps regulate our body's stress response system, making us better equipped to handle challenging situations and bounce back from setbacks. Additionally, physical activity promotes better sleep quality. When exercising, our bodies release pent-up energy and tension, making it easier to relax and fall asleep at night. Hence, regular exercise helps regulate our sleep patterns, allowing for more restorative and rejuvenating sleep.

Physical Activities That Are Good for the Brain

Boosting brain health involves more than just exercising our minds through puzzles and cognitive challenges. In fact, various stimulating activities, from brisk walks immersed in nature to the rhythmic flow of yoga practice, can unleash the brain's potential. Hence, below are an array of dynamic and captivating physical pursuits scientifically proven to nourish and optimize the brain, enabling us to unlock our full cognitive prowess and embrace a life of vitality and mental clarity.

Aerobic Exercise

Activities like running, cycling, or swimming increase heart rate and blood circulation throughout the body, including the brain. These aerobic exercises improve blood flow and provide essential oxygen and nutrients, nourishing brain cells and optimizing their functionality. Aerobic exercise, therefore, supports optimal brain health and vitality.

Moreover, aerobic exercise impacts cognitive function beyond physical fitness. Studies consistently show that regular aerobic exercise enhances cognition, memory, attention, and problem-solving skills. Additionally, aerobic exercise facilitates the production of vital neurotransmitters and growth factors in the brain. Neurotransmitters like serotonin and dopamine regulate mood, motivation, and mental well-being. Regular aerobic exercise triggers the release of these neurotransmitters, improving mood and increasing happiness. Furthermore, aerobic exercise stimulates growth factor production, such as brain-derived neurotrophic factor (BDNF), which supports neuron survival and growth, enhances synaptic plasticity, and improves overall brain function.

Likewise, improved blood flow, increased neurotransmitter production, and enhanced cognitive function due to aerobic exercise contribute to maintaining brain health and resilience as we age. Thus, making it a powerful defense against cognitive decline, preserving mental sharpness and overall cognitive well-being.

There are various aerobic exercises, such as:

Running and Jogging

Classic aerobic exercises such as running and jogging offer numerous brain optimization benefits. Regularly engaging in these activities strengthens the cardiovascular system and profoundly impacts brain health. Increased blood flow and oxygen delivery to the brain during running or jogging promote new neuron growth and enhance cognitive function. Additionally, these activities have been linked to improved mood, reduced stress levels, and enhanced memory retention. Beginners should start at a comfortable pace, gradually increasing intensity, wearing appropriate footwear, maintaining proper form, and warming up before each session. Prioritize safety by staying hydrated, running in well-lit areas, and using reflective gear during low-light conditions.

Cycling

Outdoors or indoors, cycling on a stationary bike is an excellent aerobic exercise for brain optimization. This low-impact activity provides a challenging workout while being gentle on joints. Likewise, cycling increases blood flow to the brain, improving cognitive function and focus and reducing mental fatigue. It also effectively boosts mood and relieves stress. For beginners, start with shorter rides, gradually increasing duration and intensity, ensuring proper bike fit, maintaining a steady pace, and incorporating intervals. Safety measures, such as wearing a helmet, following traffic rules, and using appropriate cycling gear, are essential.

Dancing

Having dancing as your aerobic exercise combines fun and movement, offering a range of brain-boosting benefits. From ballroom to hip-hop, dancing engages the body and mind, stimulating various brain regions simultaneously. This dynamic activity is associated with improved memory, enhanced coordination, and increased creativity. Dancing also provides an excellent way to improve cardiovascular fitness while enjoying rhythmic beats and social interaction. Beginners can explore different dance styles or join beginner-level classes. Wear comfortable footwear, warm up properly, and listen to your body to prevent injuries. Focus on proper form and gradually challenge yourself with more complex routines to reap the full benefits of this enjoyable exercise.

Choose an option that suits your preferences and fitness level, start at a comfortable pace, progress gradually, and prioritize safety precautions for a rewarding and refreshing exercise experience that keeps your brain in shape

Strength Training

Offering many benefits for physical fitness and brain health, strength training enhances cognitive function, memory, and neuroplasticity. The physical exertion involved in strength training stimulates the release of growth factors, which supports brain cell growth and survival. This leads to enhanced cognitive performance, including memory, attention, and executive functioning. Additionally, strength training promotes neuroplasticity by encouraging the formation and strengthening of neural connections, improving learning abilities, mental flexibility, and creativity.

Regular strength training exercises can help mitigate age-related cognitive decline by preserving brain volume and promoting healthy blood flow, ensuring that essential oxygen and nutrients reach the areas associated with memory and executive function. Furthermore, to optimize the benefits of strength training for the brain, adhere to *progressive overload, proper form and technique, adequate rest and recovery, and consistency.*

Progressive overload challenges the brain to continuously adapt and improve by gradually increasing exercise intensity, duration, or resistance. Ensuring **proper form and technique** during exercise helps engage targeted muscles and neural pathways effectively. At the same time, **adequate rest and recovery** between sessions allow the brain to consolidate learning and repair neural connections. Finally, maintaining a **consistent training schedule** with strength training exercises and recovery periods ensures steady brain adaptation and long-term cognitive benefits.

When designing an exercise regimen for brain optimization, focus on various exercises that target different muscle groups and stimulate multiple brain areas. Below are three categories of strength training that can help optimize your brain function.

Compound Exercises

Targeting multiple muscle groups provide a comprehensive workout that enhances overall brain health. **Squats**, a fundamental exercise, engage the lower, core, and upper body simultaneously, activating multiple muscle groups and promoting coordination. **Deadlifts**, another compound exercise, strengthen your posterior chain and challenge your grip strength and balance, activating your body and mind.

Lastly, the **bench press**, a classic upper-body exercise, targets the chest, shoulders, and triceps, promoting muscle development and enhancing neural connections.

Resistance Exercises

These exercises specifically target the upper body muscle groups for maintaining posture, stability, and physical strength. **Dumbbell rows,** where you pull weights towards your chest, effectively engage the muscles in your back, shoulders, and arms, improving posture and stability. The **shoulder press**, which involves lifting weights overhead, targets the deltoids and triceps, promoting upper body strength and stability. Additionally, **bicep curls**, a simple yet effective exercise, strengthen the biceps and forearms, improving grip strength and overall upper body power.

Core-Strengthening Exercises

A strong core not only enhances physical performance but also supports cognitive function. **Planks**, a popular exercise, engage the entire core, including the abdominal muscles, lower back, and glutes. Holding a plank position activates and strengthens these muscles, improving overall core stability. **Russian twists**, where you rotate your torso from side to side while holding a weight, target the obliques, and promote rotational stability. Meanwhile, **bicycle crunches**, a dynamic exercise, activate the abdominal muscles and promote coordination between the upper and lower body.

Incorporating these exercises into your fitness routine can optimize brain function and enhance overall cognitive abilities. Unlike cardiovascular exercises that primarily target the cardiovascular system, strength training specifically aims to increase muscle mass, enhance overall body composition, and improve functional performance.

Yoga

Practicing yoga enhances mental focus and clarity by cultivating mindfulness and present-moment awareness. As attention is directed to the breath and bodily sensations, concentration and attention span are strengthened, resulting in improved cognitive performance and sharper mental acuity.

In our fast-paced world, yoga offers effective techniques to manage stress and promote emotional well-being. Relaxation practices such as deep breathing, guided imagery, and meditation activate the body's natural relaxation response, reducing stress levels and regulating stress hormones like cortisol. This leads to emotional stability and a greater sense of inner peace.

Furthermore, yoga has a significant impact on brain plasticity, or the brain's ability to adapt and rewire itself. The combination of physical postures, breathing exercises, and meditation stimulates neural connections and activates various brain networks, enhancing brain plasticity. As a result, individuals enjoy improved cognitive function, including enhanced memory, accelerated learning, and heightened problem-solving abilities.

Yoga Poses

Among the numerous yoga poses, specific sequences stand out for their ability to stimulate and optimize brain activity, such as:

Sun Salutations (Surya Namaskar)

Sun Salutations, alternatively known as *Surya Namaskar*, constitutes a dynamic yoga sequence that serves as a rejuvenating tonic for both the body and mind. Featuring fluid movements harmoniously with deep breaths, it establishes a balanced connection between physical motion and breath awareness. This flowing series stimulates blood circulation, elevates energy levels, and enlivens the senses, thereby revitalizing the brain. Every posture within Sun Salutations aids in activating and optimizing brain function, ultimately fostering alertness and mental clarity.

Standing Poses

Mountain pose *(Tadasana)* and Warrior pose *(Virabhadrasana)* are standing poses that form the foundation of a strong and balanced yoga practice while optimizing brain function. The Mountain pose provides grounding and stability, cultivating a calm, focused mind. In contrast, Warrior poses instill strength, endurance, and concentration, empowering both body and mind.

Balancing Poses

In yoga, balancing poses offer more than physical stability; they also bring a heightened sense of mental focus and concentration. Two balancing poses renowned for their brain-boosting benefits are the Tree pose *(Vrikshasana)* and the Eagle pose *(Garudasana)*. The Tree pose improves concentration by requiring a steady gaze and balance, helping to anchor the mind and develop a sense of mental stability. Similarly, the Eagle pose promotes coordination and mental focus by simultaneously engaging both sides of the brain.

Inversions

Downward-facing Dog *(Adho Mukha Svanasana)* and Headstand *(Sirsasana)* are inversions yoga poses that position the head below the heart, enhancing blood flow to the brain and promoting optimization. The inverted V shape of the Downward-facing Dog uses gravity to boost blood circulation, improving concentration and overall brain function.

Similarly, Headstand revitalizes brain cells by increasing blood flow, promoting alertness and focus, and improving memory and problem-solving abilities. A headstand also stimulates hormone-regulating glands but requires caution and guidance from a qualified instructor to minimize injury risk.

Seated Poses

A seated or meditation pose like the Lotus *(Padmasana)* offers gentle yet effective ways to optimize the brain and foster inner peace. With its stable and grounded foundation, Lotus pose encourages mindfulness, mental clarity, and emotional balance. Likewise, it is an ideal preparatory pose for meditation, maintaining a comfortable upright posture. Mindful breathing during meditation activates the body's relaxation response, calms the mind, reduces stress and anxiety, and creates inner calm and mental peace. Regular mindfulness meditation promotes emotional well-being, resilience, and heightened self-awareness, enabling non-judgmental observation of thoughts and emotions.

Tai Chi

Tracing its roots in ancient Chinese culture, Tai Chi has evolved from a martial art into a holistic practice encompassing physical movements, meditation, and philosophical principles. The legendary Taoist monk Zhang Sanfeng is credited with its origins, as he sought harmony between the mind, body, and spirit.

Taoist principles deeply influence Tai Chi's profound philosophy, emphasizing the concept of Yin and Yang, the interconnectedness of opposing forces, and the cultivation of internal energy or Qi. Fundamental principles guiding the practice include relaxation, balance, and flowing movements, encouraging practitioners to cultivate a calm and focused mind while integrating physical and mental aspects to achieve harmony.

Characterized by slow, deliberate, and flowing movements, Tai Chi engages the entire body, promoting flexibility, balance, and coordination. The practice consists of choreographed routines or forms, with each posture seamlessly transitioning to the next. The continuous practice fosters heightened body awareness and a deep connection with one's movements. Likewise, studies have demonstrated improvements in focus, attention span, and mental clarity as the mindful nature of the practice develops heightened awareness and concentration. Additionally, Tai Chi's ability to reduce stress and anxiety is remarkable, with its slow and rhythmic movements, deep breathing, and meditative aspects promoting relaxation and calmness.

Furthermore, Tai Chi contributes to improved brain health and neuroplasticity. By engaging specific brain regions associated with cognitive function, regular practice stimulates neurogenesis—the generation of new neurons—and the formation of neural connections, ultimately fostering a more adaptive and flexible brain. Tai Chi also holds potential as a preventive measure against age-related cognitive decline, as its combination of physical movement, mental focus, and meditative elements creates an optimal environment for maintaining brain health and cognitive vitality.

Below is detailed, step-by-step guidance on how to perform Tai Chi exercises correctly.

- **Wu Chi Stance**: Position yourself with your feet shoulder-width apart, ensuring your toes are pointing forward. Relax your shoulders, elongate your spine, and slightly tuck your chin.

Keep your knees soft, maintaining a gentle bend. Visualize a subtle upward pull from the crown of your head, aligning your body in an erect posture. Allow your hands to rest comfortably at your sides or gently on your lower abdomen. Take deep breaths, establishing a sense of grounding in this relaxed yet centered stance.

- **Cloud Hands**: Assume the Wu Chi stance. Shift your weight onto your left leg while gently bending the knee. Simultaneously, extend your right foot to the side, ensuring it remains firmly grounded. Let your arms mirror the movements, generating a seamless and continuous flow. Keep your hands relaxed and slightly rounded, as if delicately holding a ball. Repeat the cycle on the other side after returning your weight to the center. Imagine your arms gracefully gliding through the air, invoking a tranquil and fluid sensation.

- **Grasp Sparrow's Tail**: Transition from the Cloud Hands position by shifting your weight onto your left leg. Extend your right foot forward, placing it on the ground as you transfer your weight. As you do this, bring your hands together in front of your chest, palms facing one another. Gradually separate your hands, moving your left hand to the left side and your right hand to the right side. Maintain a relaxed and fluid motion, as if gently grasping an object. On the opposite side, repeat the motion in the opposite direction. Balance, coordination, and inner harmony are fostered by this activity.

- **Wave Hands Like Clouds**: Commence with feet shoulder-width apart, allowing your arms to relax at your sides. Put your weight on your left foot as you advance with it. As you do so, sweep your left hand upward and across your body, simultaneously sweeping your right hand down and across your body. Visualize your hands gliding through the water, generating a seamless and undulating wave-like motion. Repeat the motion while stepping forward with your right foot, switching between your left and right feet each time. This exercise enhances flexibility, coordination, and mindful awareness.

- **Closing and Centering**: Conclude your Tai Chi practice by bringing your feet together, either touching or slightly apart. Gently rest your hands on your lower abdomen, palms facing upward. Spend a moment inhaling deeply and finding your core. Allow the accumulated energy and tranquility from the practice to permeate your body and mind. Express gratitude for the experience and the benefits it bestows. Gradually open your eyes, maintaining a sense of serenity as you transition back into your daily activities.

Remember that Tai Chi encourages awareness and inner tranquility as a form of exercise. Execute each movement gracefully, with heightened awareness and concentration on your breath. Pay close attention to your body's signals and make any required adjustments to the exercises as needed.

Dancing

Aside from being a delightful form of self-expression and physical activity that optimizes brain health, dancing offers numerous benefits beyond the dance floor, enhancing cognitive function, mood, and social well-being. As such, brain stimulation from dancing leads to increased brain activity and new neural connections. When learning dance routines, our brain's plasticity strengthens cognitive abilities and improves memory retention. Dancing also promotes spatial awareness and coordination, as intricate movements challenge our brains to harmonize with rhythm and beats, improving daily activities and physical performance. Furthermore, dancing boosts working memory and executive functions, enhancing multitasking, quick decision-making, and focused attention, all crucial for cognitive sharpness.

Moreover, dancing uplifts our spirits and enhances our mood while reducing stress. During a dance, our bodies release endorphins, which flood us with positive emotions and alleviate anxiety and tension. Likewise, it allows emotional expression, channeling energy positively and providing relaxation. Social engagement and mental stimulation are additional benefits of dancing. Participating in dance classes or group activities fosters social connections and a sense of belonging. The continuous challenge of learning and practicing various dance routines keeps our brains active and engaged, improving cognitive flexibility, creativity, and problem-solving abilities.

There are various dance styles, such as:

- **Ballet**: Recognized for its elegance, precision, and control, ballet requires a strong foundation. Begin with the basic ballet stance by standing tall with your feet turned out, heels together, and toes pointed outward. Engage your core, elongate your spine, and relax your shoulders. To perform a simple ballet movement, such as a plié, bend your knees while keeping your heels on the ground and straighten them again. Practice maintaining proper alignment and fluidity in your movements.

- **Hip-Hop**: With high-energy, rhythmic movements and urban flair, hip-hop encourages self-expression. Put your feet shoulder-width apart and adopt a relaxed stance. Allow your body to loosen up and feel the rhythm of the music. Experiment with isolating different body parts, such as your hips, chest, and arms, and practice simple footwork patterns, like the *"two-step" or "rocking."* Embrace the freedom of expression and let your personality shine through your movements.

- **Salsa**: Originating in Latin America, salsa is a vibrant partner dance that can be performed solo. While it can be performed solo, it often involves a partner. Take a comfortable stance at first, keeping your feet about hip-width apart. Test your ability to shift your weight smoothly and fluidly from one foot to the other. Incorporate hip movements and arm styling to add flair and character to your dance. As you progress, consider learning basic partner patterns, leading and following, and mastering the art of connection with a partner.

- **Contemporary**: A versatile and expressive dance style blending various forms, contemporary dance emphasizes freedom, creativity, and storytelling. Start by finding your center and grounding yourself. Experiment with different levels, such as standing, kneeling, or lying on the floor. Explore the connection between your breath and movement, allowing your body to flow and respond to the music. Embrace fluidity, release tension, and express your emotions through your dance.

Engage in a proper warm-up before dancing to prevent injuries and prepare muscles. Stretching out your major muscle groups, such as your arms, legs, neck, and back, should be your first step. Increase blood flow and mobility using dynamic exercises like shoulder rolls, side lunges, and arm circles. Keep in mind to warm up at your speed and pay attention to your body.

Choosing the Best Exercise

To optimize brain health through exercise, consider individual factors influencing preferences and capabilities. Each person possesses unique physical abilities, lifestyle constraints, and personal goals. By acknowledging these factors, we can create effective and enjoyable exercise routines.

For Males and Females

Understanding physical differences between males and females is vital when customizing exercise routines for optimal brain health. Both genders benefit from regular exercise. However, considering unique needs and preferences maximizes workout effectiveness. Males, often possessing greater upper body strength, might prefer exercises like weightlifting or high-intensity interval training (HIIT). In contrast, females may seek a balanced approach, combining cardiovascular activities with strength and flexibility training. Acknowledging these gender-specific factors ensures enjoyable and effective exercise programs for optimal brain optimization.

For Professionals

For busy professionals, incorporating physical activity into daily routines is essential for brain optimization and overall well-being. Time-efficient exercises, such as HIIT, provide practical solutions for those with limited schedules. Taking short walks or engaging in desk stretches during work breaks counteracts office environments' sedentary nature and rejuvenates the mind. Professionals seeking stress relief and mental clarity may consider options like yoga, Pilates, or mindfulness-based activities, blending physical movement and mental relaxation. Tailored exercise recommendations ensure that even the busiest individuals prioritize their brain optimization journey.

For Executives and Business Owners

Leadership demands sharp focus and effective decision-making skills. Exercise significantly impacts cognitive function, improving concentration and enhancing executive functions. Aerobic exercises like running or cycling increase blood flow to the brain, promoting new neuron growth and enhancing neural connections. This leads to improved cognitive abilities, including better memory retention, increased creativity, and enhanced problem-solving skills. By incorporating exercise into their routine, executives and business owners can optimize their mental faculties and make informed decisions with clarity and precision.

For Academics

Amidst academic demands, prioritizing physical activity is crucial. Incorporating exercise into academic routines benefits physical health and improves cognitive function. Simple strategies include taking regular movement breaks, utilizing standing desks, or participating in a group exercise to increase physical activity levels while maintaining academic productivity. Creating an environment that promotes movement and integrates exercise into daily academic life enhances cognitive abilities and academic performance.

Therefore, regular exercise is pivotal in optimizing brain function for executives, business owners, and academics. As such, it enhances focus, decision-making, concentration, and memory, positively impacting professional and academic performance.

Pillar 3:
Sleep

Sleep is a necessary process for the brain, as it consolidates memories, eliminates toxins, and recharges itself. Ensuring sufficient, restful sleep is crucial for maintaining brain health, as lack of sleep can result in cognitive impairments, emotional instability, and even chronic diseases. Prioritizing and refining our sleep patterns is essential for preserving optimal brain function.

This pillar delves into various techniques to enhance sleep quality and quantity. These methods encompass creating a bedtime routine, minimizing blue light exposure, adhering to a consistent sleep schedule, and managing stress effectively. Additionally, the book underscores the importance of optimizing factors such as temperature, noise levels, and mattress quality to foster a comfortable sleep environment.

Adopting the strategies outlined in this book can elevate our sleep patterns and support our brain health. Improved sleep leads to enhanced mental well-being, elevated moods, and a healthier, more successful life.

Chapter 4:
Sleep Hygiene and Quality

Nowadays, with screens illuminating late into the night and overflowing schedules, the significance of quality sleep is often neglected. However, amidst our hectic daily routines, remember that sleep is not just a luxury but an essential component of our well-being. Serving as a revitalizing tonic, sufficient sleep nurtures our bodies, enhances our cognitive abilities, and invigorates our spirits. The domain of slumber is where our brains consolidate memories, our immune systems rejuvenate, and our emotional resilience finds comfort. Exploring the aspects of sleep hygiene and quality uncovers the secrets to achieving restful nights, enabling us to fully wake up revitalized and prepared to embrace each new day.

How Sleep Affects Brain Health

Sleep affects our brain in various ways, including:

Sleep and Memory Consolidation

During sleep, complex neuronal activity strengthens connections between neurons, solidifying memories and boosting learning capabilities. For instance, different sleep stages impact memory consolidation uniquely. Non-rapid eye movement (NREM) sleep, including deep and lighter stages, is vital for consolidating declarative memories, such as facts and events. NREM sleep allows the brain to replay and reinforce recently acquired information, enhancing memory retention.

Conversely, rapid eye movement (REM) sleep is associated with consolidating procedural memories, including motor skills and emotional memories. The interplay between these stages optimizes memory consolidation for various information types. However, sleep deprivation significantly impairs memory and cognitive function. Insufficient sleep compromises memory consolidation and retrieval, disrupts hippocampus functioning for memory formation, and reduces memory performance.

Attention and Concentration

Adequate sleep means optimal attention and concentration. As we sleep, our brains recharge, restoring neural pathways involved in attention. Sufficient sleep sustains focus, filters out distractions, and enhances task engagement, whereas sleep deprivation leads to lapses in attention and decreased cognitive performance.

Creativity

Sleep profoundly influences creativity through memory reactivation, where recently learned information is replayed and combined with existing knowledge, fostering creative connections. Likewise, it integrates disparate ideas and forms novel associations, boosting creative thinking. Yet, lack of sleep hampers divergent thinking and limits imaginative solutions. Prioritizing quality sleep enhances creativity and unlocks innovative potential.

Emotional Well-being

Lack of sleep significantly affects mood, causing increased irritability, heightened emotional reactivity, and difficulty regulating emotions. Insufficient sleep amplifies negative emotions and hampers our ability to manage stressors due to heightened brain emotional center reactivity. Recognizing the close connection between sleep and emotional well-being underscores the need to prioritize quality sleep for a healthy mind.

Aging

During sleep, the brain undergoes essential processes supporting memory consolidation, learning, and cognitive function. Inadequate sleep in older adults is associated with an elevated risk of cognitive decline, memory loss, and neurodegenerative disorders like Alzheimer's disease. Prioritizing sleep and adopting healthy sleep habits can help older adults potentially mitigate age-related cognitive decline and promote long-term brain health.

In summary, quality sleep is a fundamental necessity for overall well-being, cognitive function, and emotional resilience. By acknowledging the profound influence of sleep on emotional well-being, brain health in aging, and the ramifications of sleep disorders, we can prioritize and optimize our sleep habits to support ideal brain function.

What Is Sleep Hygiene?

Encompassing a collection of practices and habits, sleep hygiene promotes healthy sleep patterns and ensures restful, quality sleep. For instance, it includes various factors that shape the overall sleep experience, such as the environment, behaviors, and routines related to bedtime. Integrating proper sleep hygiene into our lives can enhance both the quantity and quality of our sleep, resulting in better physical and mental well-being.

Besides that, sleep hygiene is instrumental in creating and sustaining healthy sleep patterns. Adhering to consistent sleep routines and crafting a sleep-conducive environment improves our ability to fall, remain, and achieve restorative sleep. Adopting good sleep hygiene practices can also minimize sleep disturbances and reduce the risk of sleep disorders. These practices support the synchronization of our internal body clock, or the circadian rhythm, which regulates sleep-wake cycles. Furthermore, it contributes to improved cognitive function, mood regulation, and daytime functioning, enabling us to wake up feeling refreshed and energized, ready to tackle daily challenges.

Recognizing the concept of sleep hygiene is pivotal in promoting healthy sleep patterns and quality sleep allows us to prioritize and incorporate effective strategies into our daily lives. From establishing a relaxing bedtime routine to creating a sleep-friendly environment, each aspect of sleep hygiene contributes to optimizing our sleep and unlocking the potential for improved well-being.

Common Sleep Hygiene Pitfalls

Optimizing sleep improves brain health and cognitive performance, but several common sleep hygiene pitfalls can hinder our efforts to achieve restful and rejuvenating sleep, such as:

Inconsistent Sleep Schedule

A consistent sleep schedule aids in quality sleep. Conversely, an irregular sleep schedule can disrupt our body's natural sleep-wake cycle or circadian rhythm. This inconsistency confuses the body, leading to difficulties falling asleep, poor sleep quality, and well-being impairment. Establishing a regular sleep schedule lays the foundation for improved sleep and enhanced brain function since our bodies thrive on routine.

Pre-Bedtime Electronic Device Use

Using electronic devices like smartphones, tablets, or laptops before bedtime is a widespread pitfall that negatively impacts sleep hygiene. The blue light these devices emit suppresses melatonin production, a hormone regulating sleep. As a result, pre-bedtime electronic device use disrupts the natural sleep-wake cycle and causes difficulties falling asleep and achieving restful sleep. Limiting electronic device usage near bedtime and prioritizing relaxing activities help signal the body to prepare for sleep.

Stimulant and Alcohol Consumption

Caffeine is a stimulant that can hinder falling asleep and reduce total sleep duration. Meanwhile, while alcohol may initially cause drowsiness, it disrupts the sleep cycle by decreasing rapid eye movement (REM) sleep, which is essential for memory consolidation and cognitive restoration. Avoiding evening stimulants and moderating alcohol consumption can significantly enhance sleep duration and quality, optimizing the brain's restorative processes during sleep.

Sedentary Lifestyle

A sedentary lifestyle characterized by prolonged sitting or inactivity poses a significant pitfall to brain optimization. Engaging in minimal physical activity affects our physical health and harms our cognitive function.

Leaning to a sedentary lifestyle limits the blood flow and oxygen supply to our brains, hindering their optimal functioning. Likewise, the lack of physical activity prevents the release of endorphins, which are essential for mood regulation and mental clarity. Moreover, the brain's neuroplasticity, the ability to form and strengthen neural connections, is compromised without regular movement.

Therefore, recognize the impact of a sedentary lifestyle on brain optimization and prioritize incorporating physical activity into our daily routines.

Poor Sleep Environment

Creating a conducive sleep environment helps achieve optimal brain function. However, a pitfall that many individuals overlook is a poor sleep environment. The surroundings in which we sleep can significantly impact the quality and duration of our sleep.

Factors such as noise, light, temperature, and comfort play a significant role in determining the effectiveness of our sleep environment. Excessive noise and bright lights can disrupt our sleep patterns and hinder the brain's ability to enter deep, restorative sleep phases. Similarly, an uncomfortable or overly warm sleeping environment can lead to restlessness and interrupted sleep. Hence, assess and address these environmental factors to ensure a peaceful and rejuvenating sleep environment, promoting optimal brain health and cognitive performance.

Excessive Napping

Napping can be restorative, providing a brief break and revitalizing our energy levels. Yet, excessive napping can become a pitfall to be aware of when optimizing brain function.

While short power naps can boost alertness and productivity, prolonged or frequent napping can disrupt the natural sleep-wake cycle, negatively impacting nighttime sleep quality. Subsequently, extended daytime sleep can lead to difficulty falling asleep at night, reduced sleep duration, and fragmented sleep patterns.

Furthermore, excessive napping may interfere with the brain's ability to achieve the deep, restorative stages of sleep, which are crucial for memory consolidation, learning, and overall cognitive function. To optimize brain health and sleep quality, balance the benefits of a well-timed nap and maintain a consistent and regular sleep routine.

Effects of Common Sleep Hygiene Pitfalls

When pitfalls are left unattended, it could lead to the following:

Fragmented Sleep

Characterized by frequent awakenings or difficulty staying asleep, fragmented sleep disrupts the natural sleep cycle and can harm overall well-being. When sleep is repeatedly interrupted, it prevents the body and mind from entering deep, restorative stages of sleep. As a result, individuals may experience a compromised immune system, decreased concentration, and a higher susceptibility to accidents and errors.

Increased Daytime Sleepiness and Fatigue

Neglecting proper sleep hygiene often leads to increased daytime sleepiness and fatigue. When the body does not receive adequate rest, it fails to recharge its energy reserves fully. This can manifest as persistent tiredness throughout the day, making it challenging to stay alert and focused. Individuals may struggle to stay awake during work or daily activities, risking their productivity and safety.

Impaired Cognitive Function and Memory

Quality sleep is vital for optimal cognitive function and memory consolidation. Unfortunately, poor sleep hygiene can impair these essential cognitive processes. Without sufficient rest, the brain's ability to retain and recall information becomes compromised. Individuals may experience difficulties with attention, problem-solving, and learning new concepts, hindering their overall cognitive performance.

Mood Disturbances and Irritability

Lack of proper sleep can take a toll on mental and emotional well-being. Sleep hygiene pitfalls often contribute to mood disturbances and increased irritability. When sleep-deprived, individuals are more likely to experience heightened negative emotions, such as irritability, frustration, and mood swings. Subsequently, it can strain relationships, diminish overall happiness, and reduce one's ability to cope with daily stressors.

Reduced Productivity and Performance

The consequences of poor sleep hygiene extend beyond personal well-being and affect professional and academic performance. Insufficient and fragmented sleep lead to decreased productivity and impaired performance in various tasks. Individuals may struggle to concentrate, make decisions, and meet deadlines effectively. As such, it can hinder progress, limit creativity, and ultimately undermine one's ability to achieve desired goals.

Understanding these effects underscores the importance of prioritizing good sleep hygiene practices and highlights the need for individuals to establish healthy sleep routines that promote restful, restorative sleep.

Sleep Hygiene Tips

Tailoring sleep hygiene can maximize their effectiveness and ensure that individuals of all ages can achieve restful and rejuvenating sleep.

Consistency in Sleep Schedule

In establishing healthy sleep habits, consistency is pivotal. For individuals of all ages, create a regular bedtime and wake-up time. This helps regulate the body's internal clock, known as the circadian rhythm, ensuring a smoother transition between wakefulness and sleep. Maintaining a consistent sleep routine, even on weekends, is equally essential, as disruptions in the sleep schedule can negatively impact sleep quality and overall brain function.

Creating a Sleep-Friendly Environment

Regardless of age, create a sleep-friendly environment that promotes relaxation and restfulness. Keeping the bedroom cool, dark, and quiet contributes to a conducive sleep environment. Choosing a comfortable mattress and pillows that adequately support the body is crucial for promoting a restful sleep experience. Additionally, using earplugs or eye masks to reduce noise and light disturbances can further enhance sleep quality. Maintaining a clutter-free sleep environment helps create a sense of calmness and tranquility, allowing the brain to unwind and prepare for a rejuvenating night's sleep.

Limiting Stimulants and Electronics Before Bed

Stimulants such as caffeine and nicotine can interfere with your ability to fall asleep. Avoid these substances, particularly in the hours leading up to bedtime. Instead, consider switching to decaffeinated beverages or herbal teas, which can be calming and prepare your body for rest. Meanwhile, using electronics before bed can interfere with your body's natural sleep cycle. That said, instead of using electronics, engage in calming activities such as reading a physical book, listening to soothing music, or practicing mindfulness and relaxation techniques. These activities can help your body and mind wind down, making it easier for you to fall asleep and improve the quality of your sleep.

Emphasizing Relaxation and Wind-Down Time

Optimizing brain function requires acknowledging the importance of relaxation and wind-down time in preparing the mind and body for restful sleep. Soothing activities before bed create a calming environment conducive to sleep, such as reading a captivating book or enjoying a warm bath. These activities help ease the mind and transition away from daily stresses. Practicing relaxation techniques like deep breathing or meditation further enhances the body's relaxation response, fostering tranquility and preparing you for a good night's sleep. A consistent bedtime routine, including calming rituals like soft music or herbal tea, creates a predictable and relaxing atmosphere that facilitates the transition from wakefulness to sleep.

Encouraging Regular Exercise and Physical Activity

Regular exercise benefits physical health and promotes restful sleep and optimal brain function. Daily physical activity helps regulate sleep patterns, making falling and staying asleep at night easier. Exercise releases endorphins, which alleviate stress and anxiety, improving sleep quality. However, avoid intense physical activity close to bedtime, as it may increase alertness and hinder falling asleep. Complete your exercise routine earlier, allowing the body to wind down naturally and prepare for restorative sleep.

Adopting Healthy Eating Habits

Healthy eating habits positively affect brain optimization and restful sleep. Avoid heavy meals and spicy foods close to bedtime, as they can cause discomfort and disrupt sleep. Focus on sleep-promoting foods like tryptophan-rich turkey, nuts, and seeds, which contribute to serotonin production, promoting relaxation and sleep. Incorporate magnesium-rich foods like leafy greens, legumes, and whole grains to regulate sleep patterns and promote deep, restorative sleep. Be mindful of hydration but avoid excessive fluid intake close to bedtime to minimize disruptions from frequent bathroom visits.

Managing Stress and Mental Well-being

Stress management techniques significantly impact sleep quality. Journaling, practicing mindfulness, or relaxation exercises help reduce stress and calm the mind before bedtime. Incorporating these practices into your evening routine lets you process daily events and release lingering worries or anxieties. If stress or mental health issues persistently affect your sleep, consider seeking professional help from healthcare providers or mental health professionals for tailored guidance and support.

Addressing Common Sleep Disorders

Various sleep disorders make it harder for us to get to sleep, stay asleep, or have a peaceful sleep. Yet, understanding these disorders and implementing appropriate interventions improve our sleep quality and promote better health.

Insomnia

A common sleep issue called insomnia is characterized by problems getting to sleep, staying asleep, or both. Several things, such as stress, anxiety, illnesses, or bad sleeping patterns, may bring it on. Regardless, some strategies, including cognitive-behavioral treatment (CBT-I), are used to treat insomnia. CBT-I aims to recognize and change harmful thoughts and behaviors that cause sleep problems. By implementing relaxation techniques, sleep restriction therapy (SRT), and stimulus control, individuals can experience significant improvements in their sleep patterns.

Sleep Apnea

Frequent breathing interruptions while asleep is sleep apnea. As such, it may result in disturbed sleep patterns, increased daytime sleepiness, and other health issues. Continuous positive airway pressure (CPAP) therapy is often used to address sleep apnea. This therapy involves wearing a mask connected to a machine that delivers a constant airflow to keep the airways open. While CPAP is effective, some individuals may require alternative treatments, such as oral appliances or surgery, to address the underlying causes of sleep apnea.

Restless Leg Syndrome (RLS)

An irrepressible impulse to move the legs, frequently accompanied by uncomfortable feelings, is a hallmark of restless legs syndrome. Sleep disturbances and daytime weariness may result from this illness. RLS symptoms can be controlled with a lifestyle change, such as frequent exercise and avoiding irritants like caffeine and alcohol. Medications, including dopamine agonists and anticonvulsants, may also be prescribed to alleviate symptoms and improve sleep.

Narcolepsy

Excessive daily sleepiness, an abrupt loss of muscular tone (cataplexy), and vivid, dream-like hallucinations are all symptoms of narcolepsy, a neurological condition. Even though there is no known treatment for narcolepsy, stimulants and SSRIs can assist in managing its symptoms. Developing good sleep hygiene practices, scheduling regular naps, and creating a supportive environment can also aid individuals with narcolepsy in managing their condition effectively.

In addition to addressing specific sleep disorders, incorporating restorative practices into our daily lives can enhance sleep quality. These practices include mindfulness meditation, yoga, and deep breathing exercises. Engaging in these activities before bedtime can help relax the mind and body, promoting a state of calm conducive to a restful night's sleep. Addressing sleep issues also requires establishing a relaxing sleep environment, adhering to a regular sleep schedule, and avoiding stimulating activities right before bed.

Pillar 4:
Stress Management

Life-related stress can harm the brain if it is not managed correctly. For instance, prolonged stress can result in reduced cognitive function, memory loss, and other brain-related diseases.

Given that, this pillar dives into methods that lower stress and encourage relaxation. As such, it focuses on the effects of stress on the brain and how to control it with mindfulness, meditation, exercise, and adequate sleep, among other methods. Thus, it teaches how to manage stress in our daily lives and create healthy coping mechanisms using the strategies described in it. Additionally, these strategies offer a chance to enhance general physical well-being, closely related to mental efficiency.

Putting the tactics described in this pillar into practice enhances our general quality of life and lessens stress's damaging effects on our cognitive health. This pillar's objective is to assist us in developing a healthy, balanced lifestyle that fosters the best possible brain health and mental well-being.

Chapter 5:
Protecting the Brain From Stress

Persistent stress, especially on the brain, can harm physical and emotional health. Different cognitive issues like forgetfulness and disorganization might be brought on by stress. Long-term stress can also lower the hippocampus's ability to function normally and raise the risk of dementia and Alzheimer's.

Additionally, persistent anxiety can damage the brain, leading to various mental health conditions like panic and depressive disorders. As a result, stress management is crucial for general health and well-being. This section examines the effects of stress on the brain, the necessity of managing stress, and effective stress reduction methods.

How Stress and Anxiety Affect Brain Health

Stress and anxiety are common experiences that we all face at some point. Various factors, such as work pressure, relationship issues, financial problems, and health concerns, can trigger them. While mild or occasional stress is a normal part of life, chronic stress and anxiety can significantly negatively affect brain health.

Often, stress triggers negative changes in the brain, including the shrinking of the hippocampus, which is critical for memory and learning. A study published in the journal Molecular Psychiatry found that chronic stress can cause a reduction in the volume of the hippocampus, impairing our ability to form new memories and recall old ones. Likewise, it can disrupt memory and cause inflammation in the brain, which harms brain tissue and speeds up the onset of neurodegenerative illnesses like Alzheimer's and Parkinson's. Inflammation can also disrupt communication between brain cells, affecting our mood, behavior, and cognitive function.

On the other hand, anxiety can affect brain health by increasing activity in the amygdala, a part of the brain involved in fear and emotion processing. Individuals with anxiety disorders often have increased amygdala activity compared to healthy individuals, which can contribute to developing anxiety symptoms. Neurotransmitter imbalances brought on by anxiety, including those in serotonin and dopamine, might impact mood and behavior.

Effects of Stress on Brain Health

The effects of stress on brain health are numerous and can be long-lasting. Below are some ways that stress may impact the condition of the brain:

- **Shrinking of the hippocampus**: As mentioned earlier, chronic stress can cause a reduction in the volume of the hippocampus, which can impair memory and learning.

- **Inflammation**: Chronic stress can cause brain inflammation, harming brain tissue and aiding in the emergence of neurodegenerative illnesses.

- **Anxiety and depression**: Chronic stress can cause anxiety and depression, both of which can harm the brain's health. Anxiety and depression are associated with changes in brain structure and function, particularly in brain areas involved in emotion regulation and stress response.

- **Cognitive function**: Chronic stress may impair cognitive abilities, especially in memory and concentration. According to a study published in the journal Neurology, high levels of cortisol, a stress hormone, were associated with poorer cognitive performance in older adults.

Anxiety and the Brain

Anxiety is a common mental health condition affecting brain health in various ways. Here are a few ways that anxiety has an impact on the brain:

- **Increased amygdala activity**: Individuals with anxiety disorders often have increased amygdala activity compared to healthy individuals, which can contribute to developing anxiety symptoms.

- **Changes in brain chemistry**: Neurotransmitter imbalances, including those in serotonin and dopamine, which can influence mood and behavior, have been related to anxiety.

- **Structural changes in the brain**: Chronic anxiety can lead to structural changes in the brain, particularly in areas involved in emotion regulation.

- **Cognitive function**: Anxiety can impair cognitive abilities, especially those related to attention and memory. According to a study published in the Brain and Cognition, individuals with anxiety disorders had poorer attention and memory performance than those without anxiety disorders.

- **Immune system**: Chronic stress and anxiety can also impact the immune system, leading to various health issues. Studies have shown that stress can increase inflammation in the body, which is linked to numerous chronic conditions such as cardiovascular disease, diabetes, and depression.

Importance and Benefits of Managing Stress

Although stress is a normal reaction to difficult circumstances, excessive or extended stress can harm physical and mental health. Therefore, it is essential to understand the importance of managing stress and the benefits it can bring to our lives. Likewise, stress management is of utmost importance due to the following:

- **Enhancing Physical Health**: Long-term stress exposure can cause several physical health issues, such as heart disease, high blood pressure, a weaker immune system, and digestive problems. Managing stress helps to mitigate these risks, as it allows our bodies to function optimally and reduces the likelihood of developing stress-related ailments.

- **Promoting Mental Well-being**: Stress has a huge negative impact on mental health and can cause symptoms including anxiety, depression, irritability, and trouble concentrating. By actively managing stress, we can enhance our mental well-being, improve our mood, and cultivate a positive mindset.

- **Improving Relationships**: Relationships with family, friends, and coworkers can suffer from unmanaged stress. As such, we become agitated, impatient, and less effective communicators when stressed. By managing stress effectively, we can foster healthier relationships, improve our interpersonal skills, and create a harmonious environment in our personal and professional lives.

- **Boosting Productivity**: Excessive stress can hamper our ability to focus, make decisions, and perform effectively in our daily tasks. By implementing stress management techniques, we can increase our productivity, enhance our concentration, and accomplish our goals more efficiently.

- **Enhancing Resilience**: Stress management equips us with the necessary tools and skills to navigate challenging situations and bounce back from adversity. By building resilience, we become better equipped to handle stressors and face life's inevitable ups and downs with greater ease and adaptability.

Thus, the benefits of managing stress are far-reaching and encompass our physical and mental well-being.

Stress Management Plan

A stress management plan is a collection of techniques people can employ to handle stress properly. The following techniques ought to be included in a stress management plan:

- **Identify Stressors**: Finding the sources of stress in our lives is the first step in controlling it. These stressors can be external, such as work deadlines or financial pressures, or internal, such as self-imposed expectations or negative self-talk. We can create methods to address the sources of stress by being aware of them.

- **Prioritize Self-Care**: A key component of stress management is self-care. Stress levels can be lowered by partaking in relaxing activities like routine exercise, enough sleep, and a healthy diet. Additionally, adding mindfulness techniques like deep breathing exercises or meditation can promote calmness and improve general well-being.

- **Time Management**: Poor time management can contribute to stress. By developing effective time management skills, we can prioritize tasks, set realistic goals, and allocate appropriate time for rest and rejuvenation. This enables us to manage our workload more efficiently and prevent stress from accumulating.

- **Set Boundaries**: Establishing clear boundaries in our personal and professional lives is vital for stress management. Learning to say *"no"* when necessary, delegating tasks, and avoiding overcommitment can help prevent overwhelm and create a healthier balance between work and personal lives. When we set boundaries, we protect our time and energy, allowing us to focus on what truly matters and reducing the likelihood of stress overload.

- **Practice Stress-Reducing Techniques**: Incorporating stress-reducing techniques into our daily routine can have a significant impact on our overall well-being. Some effective techniques include:

  - **Deep Breathing**: The body's relaxation response can be triggered by taking calm, deep breaths, which can help lower stress levels. We can feel calm and physically relaxed by paying attention to our breath, inhaling deeply with the nose, holding for a few seconds, and releasing slowly through the mouth.

- **Physical Exercise**: Regular physical activity lowers stress hormones and releases endorphins, the body's natural mood enhancers. Physical activity, whether a brisk stroll, yoga class, or gym session, reduces stress and fosters a sense of well-being.

- **Journaling**: It can be beneficial to express our ideas and feelings in a notebook, which helps us process our sentiments and gain perspective. We can relieve tension and get a new perspective on difficult circumstances by writing out our worries, fears, or disappointments.

- **Social Support**: Getting help from friends, family, or support groups can be a constructive way to relieve stress. Sharing our concerns and feelings with trusted individuals can offer comfort, guidance, and a sense of connection, reminding us that we are not alone in our struggles.

- **Relaxation Techniques**: Incorporating relaxation techniques such as progressive muscle relaxation, guided imagery, or listening to calming music can help promote relaxation and reduce stress. These techniques engage our senses and promote a sense of tranquility, allowing us to unwind and recharge.

- **Cultivate Healthy Coping Strategies**: Instead of resorting to unhealthy coping mechanisms like excessive alcohol consumption or emotional eating, developing healthy strategies for dealing with stress is essential. Engaging in hobbies or activities we enjoy, seeking professional help when needed, and practicing self-compassion are all healthy ways to cope with stress and build resilience.

- **Maintain a Positive Mindset**: Our thinking greatly influences how we perceive and respond to stress. By fostering a positive outlook, we can practice gratitude for the blessings in our life, reframe problems as chances for growth, and forge a robust response to stressors. Stress can be more easily managed by employing constructive self-talk and concentrating on our advantages.

- **Seek Professional Support**: If stress becomes overwhelming or persists despite our efforts, it is crucial to seek professional support. Mental health professionals can provide guidance, therapy, and additional tools to help manage and reduce stress effectively.

Pillar 5:
Social Connections

Social connection fosters cognitive health and well-being, and as social beings, social interactions are good for our brains. Brain health and a lower incidence of cognitive decline have been associated with social involvement.

The importance of forming enduring relationships with family, friends, and the community is emphasized by this pillar. Additionally, it highlights how loneliness and social isolation affect one's mental health. Loneliness has been associated with dementia, a higher risk of cognitive decline, depression, anxiety, and other mental health problems.

In this pillar, there is a strong emphasis on establishing and preserving social ties as an important aspect of brain optimization. Likewise, it also includes tips for enhancing social involvement, like joining groups, volunteering, and maintaining relationships with loved ones. Subsequently, this pillar examines how technology affects interpersonal relationships, emphasizing how essential it is to complement rather than replace in-person encounters.

Hence, to increase our cognitive performance, lower our risk of cognitive decline, and live happier, more satisfying lives by placing a higher priority on social involvement.

Chapter 6:
Relationships and Socializing

To maintain our mental and emotional health, this chapter emphasizes the value of interacting with others and forming relationships. It investigates how social interactions affect brain health, particularly how they can lessen stress and enhance cognitive ability. Moreover, it highlights the advantages of social interaction for mental health, such as preventing depression and anxiety, and offers helpful advice for forming deep relationships with people.

How Social Connections Affect Brain Health

The quality of our social connections profoundly impacts our brain health. Humans are sociable animals who thrive on interaction and human connection. Numerous studies have shown that social exclusion and loneliness can impair cognitive performance and increase the risk of brain illnesses like dementia. On the other hand, meaningful relationships and social interactions can support cognitive function and enhance brain health as we age.

One way in which social connections affect brain health is through social interaction and cognitive stimulation. When we connect with other people, we engage in conversations and activities that keep us cognitively alert. This cognitive stimulation supports the formation and maintenance of neural connections in the brain, leading to improved cognitive performance and memory retention.

For instance, participating in a group board game or stimulating conversation with a friend can provide the cognitive exercise that keeps the brain sharp. Moreover, social ties can relieve stress and provide emotional support, both beneficial for brain health. Social support from family and friends helps reduce stress levels and the likelihood of developing mental health issues such as depression and anxiety. These conditions have been linked to a higher risk of dementia and a decline in cognitive ability. Therefore, social relationships can enhance brain health by reducing stress and offering emotional support.

Conversely, loneliness and social isolation can have detrimental effects on brain health. According to a study, loneliness raises the possibility of developing dementia and cognitive impairment. This is partly because lonely individuals are less likely to engage in stimulating social and cognitive activities. Additionally, loneliness can contribute to higher levels of stress and depression, which can negatively impact brain health.

To enhance brain health, prioritize meaningful relationships and social ties. As such, take several steps to **develop and preserve your social connections**. Joining clubs or social groups that share our interests is a good technique. Being part of a social group, such as a reading club or a hiking club, not only provides cognitive stimulation but also fosters lasting relationships, enhancing overall well-being and reducing the risk of social isolation. Likewise, participating in these groups offers opportunities for social interaction, which can reduce the risk of cognitive decline.

Subsequently, **keeping in touch with family and friends** is essential for maintaining social relationships and promoting brain health. Regular communication through text messages, social media, or phone calls can provide emotional support and reduce stress, which are important factors that can influence cognitive function. Besides that, a strong social support network can also help individuals navigate life's challenges, such as aging or illness, which can impact brain health. By nurturing relationships with loved ones, we can support our mental and emotional well-being and enhance our brain health.

Another effective strategy for enhancing the mind and body, particularly the health of the brain, is **volunteering**. Helping others increases our sense of self-worth and fosters social connections, which can lower the risk of cognitive decline. Volunteering also provides a sense of accomplishment and purpose, which can contribute to overall well-being and mental health. Likewise, volunteering allows us to challenge ourselves, discover new abilities, stimulate our minds, and promote personal growth.

Attending social gatherings is another effective approach to making friends and supporting mental health. Participating in events like concerts, parties, or community gatherings offers chances to make friends and stimulate your mind. Social gatherings can also bring a sense of pleasure and community, enhancing overall well-being.

Engaging in activities related to our interests and hobbies can also lead to new connections and the development of social networks. Participating in social events aligned with our passions can support our cognitive health and maintain a sense of community.

Remember that loneliness and social isolation can significantly impact physical and mental health. If left unaddressed, these conditions can have detrimental effects on brain health. Therefore, if you are feeling lonely or socially isolated, it is imperative that you get professional help. A mental health professional can assist in developing skills for forming deep connections and helping identify and address the underlying causes of social isolation. Additionally, they can offer advice on dealing with any underlying mental health problems that might be causing the loneliness.

Thus, meaningful connections and social interactions stimulate the mind, ease stress, and offer emotional support, improving brain health. On the other hand, loneliness and social isolation can negatively affect cognitive performance and increase the risk of brain illnesses. Therefore, it is essential to prioritize and nurture our social connections. Likewise, humans are social beings, and our brains thrive on connection. By prioritizing social connections and engaging in meaningful interactions, we can support our brain health and lead fulfilling lives.

Mental Health Benefits of Being Social

Humans are inherently social beings, and throughout history, social interaction has played a vital role in our lives. As members of society, our identities are shaped by our interactions with others, and our mental and physical well-being is greatly influenced by social engagement. Connecting gives us various advantages, such as consolation, inspiration, shared experiences, and perspective. In this section, we will delve into the specific benefits of social engagement for mental health, explore the reasons behind our social nature, and examine how social interaction affects our overall wellness.

Evolutionarily, our exceptional social nature has been essential to our survival and development as a species. Over millions of years, our ancestors evolved sophisticated social abilities and behaviors that allowed them to flourish in their environments. A study published in the journal Nature highlighted the significance of sociality for the early hominids' survival.

Developing a rudimentary language among early hominids facilitated effective communication and idea-sharing, enabling successful collaboration and the creation of advanced tools and technologies. The exchange of ideas and knowledge among individuals played a pivotal role in the growth of human civilization, as it allowed us to build upon past discoveries and innovations.

Empathy and compassion, intrinsic qualities of our species, have also contributed to our success. Researchers propose that humans are inherently kind creatures, and this innate quality has enabled us to survive and thrive in challenging situations. Our capacity for understanding and empathy has allowed us to develop close relationships and cooperate in problem-solving.

The emergence of human culture and society has heavily relied on compassion and empathy, as demonstrated by the development of social institutions and support systems to assist the less fortunate. From social welfare and charity to healthcare and education, these organizations exemplify our innate impulse to help others and improve the world.

Our social nature has played a significant role in the success of our species. In addition to our ability to forge close social bonds and construct fair and equitable societies, the evolution of language and social behavior has facilitated more effective collaboration. As we adapt to changing circumstances, our social nature will likely remain essential to what defines us as humans.

One of the remarkable effects of social interaction on our mental health is its ability to influence our stress response. When we connect with others, specific regions of our nervous system release a "cocktail" of neurotransmitters that regulate how we react to stress and anxiety.

Renowned psychologist Susan Pinker explains that face-to-face interaction triggers a cascade of neurotransmitters that protect us in the present and contribute to long-term stress resilience. A simple act like shaking hands or giving a high-five can release oxytocin, a hormone that enhances trust and reduces cortisol levels, alleviating tension. Additionally, social interaction promotes the production of dopamine, a naturally occurring opioid that acts as a painkiller and induces a pleasurable sensation.

Research has linked the human inclination for social interaction to numerous mental and physical health benefits. Recent studies have shown that social engagement can significantly alleviate physical pain and improve health outcomes for individuals undergoing medical treatment. For example, a 2021 National Institute of Health study found that romantic touch can substantially reduce physical suffering. The agony was greatly diminished when one partner placed their hand on the other's arm while both experienced mild pain. Hence, the researchers hypothesized that the touch of a loved one triggers the body's natural painkillers, fostering feelings of security and comfort.

Similarly, social support has been found to improve the health outcomes of cancer patients undergoing chemotherapy. A study published in the Journal of Clinical Oncology revealed that cancer patients with access to social interaction and support tended to fare better during treatment than those without such support. Patients who participated in support groups reported less discomfort and nausea, enhanced mood and overall quality of life.

The sense of belonging and emotional connection that comes from social support can alleviate feelings of loneliness and isolation, which are especially crucial in times like the Covid-19 pandemic when social distancing measures have resulted in increased social isolation.

Furthermore, the benefits of being socially engaged extend beyond physical health and mental well-being. Social interaction can create a sense of community, reduce loneliness, and enhance overall mental health and happiness. When we engage with others, we feel a sense of purpose and belonging, as if we are part of something greater than ourselves. This sense of significance and community is essential for our mental and emotional well-being, providing security and support.

The effects of social interaction on the brain are also noteworthy. Studies have demonstrated that engaging in social interactions can profoundly impact our cognitive abilities and brain health. Social interaction and motivation have been shown to enhance memory encoding and retrieval while protecting the brain against neurodegenerative disorders. When we interact with others, we are exposed to new ideas, perspectives, and knowledge, which can stimulate the growth of new abilities and expand our cognitive capacities. Social interaction can stimulate the brain's plasticity, allowing for the development of new neural connections and providing a protective effect against conditions like Alzheimer's disease.

Collaborating with others on projects or engaging in conversations about various subjects can strengthen memory formation and enhance long-term memory. Social motivation and touch also play a significant role in maintaining clear thinking and overall brain health. Likewise, it can elevate mood, reduce stress, and alleviate anxiety, positively affecting cognitive performance.

Therefore, engaging with others improves our memory, protects against neurodegenerative disorders, and helps us acquire new skills and knowledge through the expertise of others. Actively prioritizing social connections daily is essential to reap these benefits and enhance our overall cognitive function.

Tips to Build Brain-Boosting Connections

Maintaining physical health is often considered more important than social interaction for our mental health. However, studies have shown that social engagement is essential for brain health and helps strengthen brain connections, increase memory, and concentration. This section will discuss the benefits of social interaction for mental health, ways to create connections that will help our brains, and how close relationships can promote brain health.

Social Interaction and Brain Development

Social interaction can stimulate our brains and support the development of neural networks. When we interact with others, we practice our cognitive skills and activate the brain's reward areas. For instance, our brains release dopamine when we laugh and speak, which makes us feel good and lifts our spirits.

We can also pick up new information and be exposed to various viewpoints through social interaction. Studies have indicated that individuals who are more socially active tend to have superior cognitive abilities in their later years, demonstrating the long-term benefits of this increase in mental engagement.

Creating Social Connections

Maintaining social connections as we age can be difficult. Over time, friendships may fade, and family members frequently become preoccupied with their lives.

However, there are several methods to resume social connection despite these obstacles. Reestablishing contact with long-lost friendships is one of the easiest methods to create satisfying partnerships. You can frequently take up where you left off with minimal effort since you have a shared past.

Social media can make it simple to reconnect with old friends and find people from your past. Alternatively, look through your address book and call the person on the phone.

Relationship Quality Matters

Not all relationships are made equal. Interpersonal connections that are stressful might actually harm your health. According to a study from 2021 that appeared in the Journal of the American Heart Association, women who reported feeling a lot of social pressure were more likely than those who didn't over the course of 15 years to develop major heart issues.

Although the focus of this study was not on brain health, there are several risk factors in common between cardiovascular disease and cognitive decline. Intense relationships have also been related in other research to other physical or mental health issues.

Instead of attempting to increase the number of people in your social circle by integrating people who deplete you, it is preferable to devote your time to a small number of relationships that calm and fulfill you.

Staying in Touch

Along with face-to-face encounters, there are numerous internet options for staying in touch with friends and family. A good technique to stay in touch is to email close ones or make a video chat to a pal on a smartphone.

Numerous communities and libraries provide free or inexpensive social gathering places online, including reading clubs, public forums, and creative classes. You can be directed to a variety of resources like these through your local library or senior center.

In the end, the more receptive you are to new things and people, the more probable it is that you will develop relationships with people who can support your continued good health.

Interaction With Others and Cognitive Health

Maintaining close relationships with friends and family and engaging in worthwhile social activities may help people retain their cognitive abilities longer and prevent cognitive decline as they age.

Some studies have found that older adults who are socially active have a lower risk of developing cognitive decline and dementia than those who are less socially active. By offering possibilities for learning and growth, emotional support, and mental stimulation, social interaction may aid to improve brain function.

The risk of cognitive decline is known to be increased by stress and despair, both of which can be reduced by social ties.

It is important to note that there is not conclusive data connecting social participation and cognitive health. To fully understand the link between social involvement and cognitive decline, as well as the processes through which social engagement may aid in brain protection, more research is required.

However, despite the limitations in studying the impact of social engagement on mental health, the evidence suggests that older adults' cognitive function and brain health may be influenced by their social connections, as well as the type, quality, and purpose of their relationships.

Benefits of Social Interaction on Brain Health

While the exact mechanisms are not fully understood, social interaction has been associated with numerous benefits for brain health. Meaningful relationships and social contacts can improve brain health as we age, while loneliness and social exclusion can degrade cognition and increase the risk of dementia.

Social ties can reduce stress and provide emotional support, preventing the emergence of mental health issues like depression and anxiety. Moreover, the creation and maintenance of neural connections in the brain are supported by cognitive stimulation and social contact, improving cognitive function and memory retention.

Strategies to Build Brain-Boosting Connections

To build brain-boosting connections and enhance mental well-being, consider implementing the following strategies:

- **Become a member of clubs or social organizations:** Participating in activities or joining groups that share your interests might open up social interaction opportunities. You can find like-minded people in any community organization, whether it be a reading club, sports team, interest group, or other activity.

- **Uphold current connections:** Keep up the connections you already have with family and friends. Spend time with them, interact frequently with them, and demonstrate a sincere interest in and concern for their welfare.

- **Volunteer:** Volunteering not only benefits society but also provides an opportunity to make new friends and lasting connections. Find volunteer opportunities in your neighborhood that fit your interests and passions.

- **Participate in social meetings**, parties, neighborhood activities, or local festivals by attending them. You can increase your social network and meet new individuals at these gatherings.

- **Ask for expert assistance if necessary:** Don't be afraid to ask for help from a professional if you have trouble making friends or feel lonely. To assist you overcome any obstacles and enhance your social engagement, mental health specialists can offer direction and support.

The Impact of Loneliness on Brain Health

People of different ages and socioeconomic levels can feel the ubiquitous and uncomfortable emotion of loneliness. The subjective experience of social isolation or a lack of companionship is what is referred to as it, and it can have a serious negative effect on both mental and physical health.

One of the primary ways in which loneliness affects brain health is through its impact on the stress response. Chronic loneliness has been shown to activate the hypothalamic-pituitary-adrenal (HPA) axis, which controls the body's response to stress. This activation can lead to a dysregulated stress response, with a cascade of negative effects on the brain and body. Chronic stress, for instance, can alter the structure and operation of the brain, affecting cognition and memory. Additionally, it can raise the risk of mental health conditions like anxiety, depression, and others.

In addition to the stress response, loneliness can also affect brain health through its impact on sleep. Poor sleep is a common consequence of loneliness, with individuals reporting shorter and more fragmented sleep patterns. This sleep disturbance may have a negative impact on mood, cognition, and general health. For instance, research has demonstrated a link between inadequate sleep and a higher risk of dementia and cognitive deterioration.

Furthermore, social isolation and loneliness have been linked to increased inflammation in the body, which can have negative effects on brain health. Inflammation is a key contributor to the development of neurodegenerative diseases, such as Alzheimer's and Parkinson's disease. Inflammation can also lead to the loss of brain tissue and impair cognitive function.

Research has also suggested that loneliness can affect the brain's reward centers, which are responsible for processing pleasure and motivation. The brain releases chemicals like dopamine and oxytocin, which encourage feelings of happiness and well-being, when people experience social connection and support. Chronic loneliness, on the other hand, might stifle this reaction and reduce the brain's capacity for motivation and pleasure.

Loneliness' effects on the brain can have a substantial impact on one's general health and well-being. For instance, research has demonstrated that lonely people are more likely to experience a variety of physical health issues, such as cardiovascular disease, stroke, and chronic pain. Additionally, they are more likely to indulge in hazardous habits like smoking and binge drinking.

It is important to note that loneliness and social isolation are not the same thing, although they are often used interchangeably. In contrast to loneliness, which is a more purely subjective condition of feeling cut off from people, social isolation is the objective situation of having few social interactions.

It is possible to be socially isolated without feeling lonely, and the reverse is also true. Social isolation can be a risk factor for loneliness.

To address the impact of loneliness on brain health, it is important to focus on promoting social connections and support. This can include efforts to strengthen existing relationships, as well as opportunities to build new ones. For example, joining social groups, volunteering, and participating in community activities can all be effective ways to combat loneliness.

Mental health interventions, such as cognitive-behavioral therapy, can also assist people in creating coping mechanisms to deal with feelings of social isolation and loneliness.

The Role of Social Support in Stress Management

Stress has become a typical occurrence for many people in our fast-paced and demanding environment. However, the availability of social support can be extremely important for how we experience and handle stress. Social support is the emotional, intellectual, and practical support others offer you when you need it most. Our capacity to manage stress and advance general well-being can be considerably impacted by the availability of social support networks.

One of the primary roles of social support in stress management is its ability to buffer the negative effects of stress on our physical and mental health. A sense of comfort, security, and understanding can be had when we are dealing with difficult situations thanks to supporting relationships.

According to a growing body of evidence, people with strong social support networks typically experience less stress and enjoy better overall health (Cohen & Wills, 1985). Think of a person who is experiencing a challenging time at work, for instance. Having colleagues or friends who offer empathy, advice, and assistance can help alleviate the stress and provide a sense of solidarity.

Social support can also play a role in helping us reframe our stressors and develop more adaptive coping strategies. When we discuss our stressors with supportive individuals, they may provide alternative perspectives or offer suggestions for managing the situation.

This external feedback can broaden our understanding of the stressor and provide us with new strategies to cope effectively. For instance, a person experiencing financial stress may seek advice from a trusted friend who has successfully navigated similar challenges. This guidance can lead to the exploration of new opportunities, financial planning, or accessing relevant resources.

Furthermore, social support can enhance our self-esteem and confidence, which are vital components of stress management. When we feel supported and valued by others, we develop a sense of self-worth and belief in our ability to handle stressors. This increased self-esteem can boost our resilience and make us more equipped to face and overcome challenges.

Real-life examples of this can be seen in sports teams, where players often rely on the encouragement and support of their teammates and coaches to perform at their best under pressure.

Social support can offer tangible aid in addition to emotional support during trying circumstances. This can include tangible forms of help, such as lending a hand with tasks, providing resources, or offering financial assistance. For instance, a person going through a major life transition, such as moving to a new city, may greatly benefit from the practical support of friends or family members who help with the logistics of the move. This practical assistance can alleviate the burden of stress and enable individuals to focus on adapting to the new circumstances more effectively.

It is important to note that the quality and nature of social support can vary among individuals and across different contexts. One person may not respond the same way to something that another finds to be supportive. Therefore, it is crucial to have diverse sources of social support and cultivate relationships that align with our needs and preferences. This can involve seeking support from family, friends, colleagues, or even support groups or professional counselors.

Balancing Socializing and Personal Boundaries

In our increasingly interconnected world, socializing plays a significant role in our overall well-being. Engaging with others, forming connections, and nurturing relationships are important aspects of a fulfilling life. Establishing and upholding personal limits, however, is equally crucial to ensuring a good balance between socializing and self-care. Balancing socializing and personal boundaries allow us to prioritize our needs, maintain authenticity, and foster healthy relationships.

Setting personal boundaries is crucial for maintaining our emotional and mental well-being. It involves clearly defining our limits, preferences, and values in terms of how we interact with others and how we allocate our time and energy. By establishing these boundaries, we protect ourselves from becoming overwhelmed or feeling depleted. For example, setting boundaries around the amount of time we spend socializing each week can prevent burnout and help us maintain a healthy balance between social activities and personal time for rest and rejuvenation.

Prioritizing our wants and ideals also comes from striking a balance between socializing and personal boundaries. It enables us to better match our social interactions with our individual objectives and aspirations.

For instance, if we value personal growth and learning, we may choose to engage in social activities that provide opportunities for intellectual stimulation and meaningful conversations. By being intentional about our social engagements, we ensure that our time spent socializing contributes positively to our personal growth and well-being.

Maintaining personal boundaries in socializing also enables us to cultivate authenticity and genuine connections. When we have clear boundaries, we are more likely to express our true selves and engage in relationships that align with our values and beliefs. Authenticity fosters deeper connections and allows us to attract and maintain relationships that support our personal growth and happiness.

By honoring our boundaries, we create a space where we can be true to ourselves, and form connections based on mutual respect and understanding.

It is important to remember that setting personal boundaries does not mean isolating ourselves or avoiding social interactions. Rather, it involves being mindful of our needs, limitations, and comfort levels. It allows us to engage in social activities that bring us joy and fulfillment while respecting our individuality.

By doing so, we create a healthy balance that allows us to enjoy the benefits of socializing without sacrificing our well-being.

Real-life examples of balancing socializing and personal boundaries can be seen in various contexts. For instance, in the workplace, individuals may set boundaries around their availability for socializing during work hours to maintain focus and productivity. In friendships, setting boundaries around personal space and privacy can contribute to a stronger and more respectful bond.

Even in romantic relationships, individuals may establish boundaries around personal time and hobbies to ensure a healthy balance between togetherness and individuality.

Effective communication is key to balancing socializing and personal boundaries. By openly expressing our needs, limitations, and preferences to others, we can create mutual understanding and respect. Communicating our boundaries allows others to adjust their expectations and behavior accordingly. Additionally, it encourages open and honest conversation, creating a social climate that is nurturing and helpful.

Chapter 7:
Connecting It All Together

Making good lifestyle decisions as you age aids in maintaining mental acuity and enhancing cognitive capacities. As such, this chapter presents a thoughtful approach to integrating wholesome practices into your routine, fostering an environment conducive to holistic well-being. With the right blend of physical and mental wellness strategies, you are on your way to unlocking an elevated quality of life. Let this be your starting point in creating a healthier, more balanced lifestyle.

Incorporating Brain Optimization Into Daily Life

To incorporate brain optimization into your life, do the following:

Set Goals and Track Your Progress

To optimize our brain's potential and increase our chances of success, setting goals and tracking our progress can be a scientifically validated method. Goal setting has been extensively studied and proven to have a profound impact on the way our brain functions. By understanding how goals affect the brain, we can harness this power to reorganize our brain cells and enhance our cognitive abilities.

In this section, we will explore the relationship between goal setting and brain optimization, the structural changes that occur in the brain, the types of goals that are most effective, and the importance of monitoring progress.

When we set goals, our brain's amygdala, responsible for emotions, determines the importance of the goal to us. Simultaneously, the frontal lobe, responsible for problem-solving, helps us define the specific details and implications of the goal.

Together, these regions of the brain keep us focused on behaviors and situations that align with our objectives while ignoring distractions that hinder our progress.

Remarkably, goal setting has been found to alter the brain's structure. In a groundbreaking study at the University of Texas involving individuals with multiple sclerosis (MS), researchers discovered that those who set challenging wellness goals experienced fewer and milder symptoms compared to a control group. This finding suggests that goal setting can facilitate brain recovery even in the face of degenerative brain diseases.

By setting goals, we can create a neural environment that supports our aspirations.

Researchers have also identified the types of goals that significantly impact the brain's structure. According to research in the Journal of Experimental Psychology (2019), people frequently underestimate how challenging emotional objectives are.

When we are highly motivated to succeed, our brains minimize the importance of obstacles, making them appear less significant than they actually are. Consequently, setting emotionally charged goals can rewire our brain in a way that enhances our chances of success.

Furthermore, research has shown that difficult goals are more motivating than easy ones. Setting ambitious goals, such as cutting energy consumption by 20%, has been found to be more effective in driving behavioral change than setting easier goals.

In an experiment published in the Journal of Applied Psychology (2019), individuals who committed to a difficult goal were able to achieve energy savings, while those who set an easier goal only maintained their previous consumption levels. By setting challenging goals, we can fully engage our amygdala and frontal lobe, thereby increasing our brain's capacity for success.

However, it is important to note that goal setting is most effective when it considers the unique characteristics of the individual.

A leader, for example, cannot impose goals on their team members and expect them to experience the same brain-altering effects. Each person must set their own high-stakes objectives, considering their individual aspirations and motivations.

Once we have established challenging goals, it becomes crucial to monitor our progress. By tracking our progress, we can evaluate how far we have come and identify areas for improvement.

Monitoring allows us to understand what is working and what needs adjustment, enabling us to modify our strategies accordingly. For instance, if our goal is to lose 20 pounds, keeping a food journal, weighing ourselves regularly, and recording post-workout feelings can help us assess our progress.

If we are not seeing the desired results after a few weeks, we can adjust our workout routine or caloric intake.

Progress tracking is a source of inspiration as well. Seeing how far we have come instills a sense of achievement and inspires us to continue pushing forward. Conversely, tracking helps us identify areas where we need to improve and creates a sense of urgency to make necessary adjustments if progress is lacking.

Depending on the nature of the goal, many methods can be used to track progress. For financial goals, tracking expenses and income using spreadsheets for budgeting apps can be effective.

For skill acquisition, establishing milestones and recording the time devoted to training can provide a clear measure of progress. By tailoring the monitoring approach to fit our specific objectives, we can effectively track our advancement.

Monitoring progress not only helps us stay accountable but also provides a valuable opportunity to identify areas for improvement. When we have a record of what we have done or haven't done, it becomes harder to make excuses for lack of progress.

This is particularly useful when working with a coach or mentor who can help us stay on track and provide guidance along the way.

While tracking progress is essential, it is crucial to strike a balance and avoid becoming overly fixated on numbers and details. It is simple to become mired in the details and overlook the greater picture.

Finding a monitoring system that works for us and is not overly time-consuming is vital. The goal is to have a tool that supports our efforts without becoming a burden or distraction.

Build a Brain-Friendly Lifestyle

Developing a brain-friendly lifestyle is crucial for maintaining physical and intellectual fitness as we age. Science and technology have shed light on the significant role that lifestyle factors play in preserving brain health. While we may not be able to prevent all types of memory loss, there are proactive measures we can take to safeguard and enhance our brains. In this section, we will explore various strategies such as regular exercise, a nutritious diet, sufficient sleep, mental challenges, and social interaction that contribute to building a brain-friendly lifestyle.

A healthy brain is maintained by engaging in regular exercise. Engaging in physical activity promotes the creation of new brain cells and synapses, while also increasing blood flow and oxygen availability to the brain.

However, it is important to ensure that our blood contains an adequate amount of iron for the brain to fully benefit from exercise. Including iron-rich foods in our diet, such as dried fruit, green leafy vegetables like spinach, fortified cereals, and pulses like baked beans, can support optimal brain function.

Adopting a balanced diet is crucial for a healthy brain in addition to exercise. A diet high in colorful fruits and vegetables and low in saturated fats has many advantages for the health of the brain. Oily fish, high in omega-3 fatty acids, helps reduce brain inflammation and promotes the growth of new brain cells.

Studies have shown that individuals who consume fish at least once a week have a decreased risk of dementia compared to those who do not. Rather than focusing on specific nutrients, it is advisable to consume a variety of meals to benefit from a wide range of nutrients that support brain health.

Alzheimer's disease and cognitive decline have been linked to a lower risk with the Mediterranean diet. This diet includes high intakes of fruits, vegetables, beans and peas, complex carbohydrates, and seafood.

Using red wine and olive oil as primary sources of fat during dinner is another characteristic of this brain-friendly diet . By adopting a Mediterranean-inspired diet, we can make our journey towards a brain-friendly lifestyle pleasurable and enjoyable.

The proper functioning of the brain depends on sleep. Our brains consolidate and process the knowledge we have acquired throughout the day as we sleep, encoding memories into neural circuits.

Lack of sleep can affect attention span and cause delayed responses to unanticipated events. To optimize sleep and brain health, it is important to relax mentally before bedtime, avoid the use of electronic devices that emit blue light, eat small and frequent meals throughout the day instead of late-night binge eating, and limit the consumption of caffeinated beverages.

In addition to physical and dietary considerations, mental challenges are crucial for maintaining a healthy brain. Regular mental exercise helps increase cognitive reserve and keeps the brain sharp.

As cognitive decline is a normal aspect of aging, it becomes even more important to engage in activities that challenge the brain. Activities such as solving puzzles, participating in debates or discussions with friends, and learning a new language can test and enhance our mental stamina.

Social interaction is equally essential for a healthy brain. Humans are social creatures, and research has consistently shown that regular social engagement can lower the risk of cognitive decline and dementia.

Activities such as meeting up with friends for coffee, attending parties, or volunteering offer numerous benefits for the brain, including enhanced cognition and memory, reduced dementia risk, and improved mental health. Social engagement stimulates the brain, strengthens neural connections, and enhances overall brain function.

Social interaction and a lowered risk of cognitive decline have been demonstrated to be significantly correlated in studies. Individuals with higher levels of social engagement have been shown to have a 70% reduced risk of cognitive decline compared to those who are less socially active.

Furthermore, being socially active can lower the likelihood of experiencing moderate cognitive impairment, which is often a precursor to dementia.

In addition to its impact on brain health, socializing also has positive effects on mental well-being. Engaging in social activities, volunteering, and spending time with close friends and family can reduce stress and anxiety, improve mood, and enhance feelings of happiness and well-being.

It is evident that social connection plays a crucial role in maintaining both mental and brain health.

Incorporating social interaction into our daily routine can be achieved in various ways. Joining clubs or groups that align with our interests, such as hiking or book clubs, provides opportunities to meet like-minded individuals and engage in stimulating conversations.

Attending social gatherings such as concerts or festivals and volunteering for local nonprofits are also effective ways to connect with others and contribute to the community. Even simple activities like taking a walk with a neighbor or meeting a friend for coffee can have a positive impact on our social engagement and brain health.

It is important to note that building a socially active lifestyle should not be viewed as a chore, but rather as an enjoyable and fulfilling endeavor. Finding activities that genuinely interest us and bring us joy is key to maintaining long-term engagement.

If we are struggling to come up with enjoyable social activities, we can explore new hobbies or seek recommendations from friends and family. It is never too late to start developing a more socially active lifestyle that nurtures our brain and enhances our overall well-being.

In addition to socializing, mental stimulation is vital for brain health. Taking part in mentally demanding activities enhances memory, cognition, and general brain health.

Activities such as reading, solving puzzles, acquiring new skills, or enrolling in classes are effective ways to keep our brains active and stimulated. Learning a new language, for example, has been shown to boost memory, cognitive function, and even prevent the onset of dementia.

Beyond the cognitive benefits, learning a new language also provides personal growth and a sense of accomplishment.

Another crucial component of a lifestyle that is good for the brain is physical activity. Numerous advantages of exercise are available for both physical and emotional well-being. In terms of brain health, exercise enhances synaptic connections, increases blood flow to the brain, and promotes the production of neurotransmitters like dopamine and endorphins, which are known to boost mood and cognitive function.

It is worth noting that even light exercise, such as cycling or walking, can have significant benefits for the brain. Consequently, frequent exercise must be a part of our daily routine to maintain a lifestyle that is brain friendly.

To build a brain-friendly lifestyle, it is crucial to consider all these factors holistically. Regular exercise, a nutritious diet, sufficient sleep, mental challenges, and social interaction should all be integrated into our daily lives.

We may actively enhance brain health and lower the risk of cognitive decline by doing these behaviors. Moreover, building a brain-friendly lifestyle not only enhances our cognitive abilities but also contributes to overall well-being and a higher quality of life.

Create a Supportive Environment

It is essential to create a supportive environment if we want to improve our emotional and physical health. Our environment plays a significant role in our cognitive development, and research has shown that being surrounded by greenery, particularly during childhood, can positively impact our brain's cognitive abilities.

The color green symbolizes life and nature, where we find harmony and vitality. In this section, we will explore how being in the presence of greenery affects our brains and discuss various ways to foster a positive environment.

During childhood, when the brain is rapidly developing, the environment in which we grow up can have a profound impact on the condition of our minds and their potential.

A study titled *Nature and Neurodevelopment: Differences in Brain Volume by Residential Exposure to Greenness* (2022), revealed that the more exposure children have to natural vegetation, the more their cognitive regions mature. MRI scans of 263 children between the ages of 7 and 9 showed that those who had greater contact with nature had stronger cognitive skills.

This highlights the importance of incorporating nature into our surroundings to support optimal brain development.

Living in a green environment offers numerous advantages, with one of the most significant being its positive impact on cognitive development. Being surrounded by trees and other natural features has a surprisingly beneficial effect on our minds.

The presence of greenery promotes focus, meditation, and contemplation, providing a sense of peace and tranquility. Living in a quiet and green environment is essential for maintaining harmony, as it enhances our cognitive abilities. The color green, representing nature, acts as a catalyst for promoting overall well-being.

In urban settings, where children are exposed to air pollution, noise, and other elements that can hinder healthy brain development, it becomes even more critical to establish a psychophysical connection with nature. The research conducted by Wendee Nicole (2019), emphasizes the need to make green spaces more accessible to people, especially children, as this period of life is crucial for brain development.

We may put the following strategies into practice to foster a supportive environment:

- **Greener cities**: Given that metropolitan areas are where most people live, it is crucial that cities become greener. By incorporating accessible playgrounds, parks, and an abundance of trees, cities can enhance their beauty while also benefiting the health and well-being of their inhabitants.

- **Plants and healthier air**: The air we breathe is a vital component of our overall health, oxygenating our blood and minds. However, we often underestimate the importance of clean air within our homes. Smoke, cooking emissions, and dust can create a harmful compound indoors. By introducing plants into our living spaces, we can help purify the air. There are numerous plant varieties known for their air-purifying properties, offering a natural solution to improve indoor air quality.

- **Walking in nature**: Engaging in nature walks is a fantastic way to connect with the natural world and improve both our physical and mental well-being. It serves as a delightful and healthful activity that allows us to escape the pollutants of the city. The benefits of spending time in nature are tremendous, and it does not require significant effort to access these natural environments.

- **Establishing a green workspace**: Creating a green workspace can enhance our well-being and productivity. Adding plants to our desks, incorporating green paint on the walls, and having windows that provide views of greenery can significantly improve our office environment. Research has shown that being in the presence of plants while working can reduce stress, increase focus, and boost overall job satisfaction.

- **Surrounding ourselves with supportive individuals**: A supportive environment encompasses not only our physical surroundings but also the people who inhabit it. Surrounding ourselves with positive influences can greatly impact our mental and physical well-being. Supportive individuals are attentive to our needs, offer guidance when necessary, and provide assistance when we face challenges. They foster a feeling of welcome and inclusion that fosters a supportive environment. Social ties are crucial for preserving resilience and overall well-being, according to research.

When we have a support network of encouraging individuals, we experience a range of benefits. We feel validated and understood, reducing feelings of isolation and loneliness. Supportive relationships provide emotional stability and act as a buffer against stress. Sharing our experiences, concerns, and joys with trusted individuals fosters a sense of connection and strengthens our mental and emotional resilience.

Supportive individuals also play a crucial role in our personal growth and development. They provide constructive feedback, challenge our perspectives, and encourage us to step out of our comfort zones. Their belief in our abilities motivates us to pursue our goals and aspirations. By surrounding ourselves with positive influences, we create an environment that nurtures our personal growth and empowers us to overcome obstacles.

Maintaining helpful relationships requires active cultivation. Here are some strategies to foster a network of encouraging individuals:

- **Seek out like-minded communities**: Joining groups or communities that align with our interests and values can provide opportunities to connect with supportive individuals. Whether it is a hobby club, a professional association, or an online community, interacting with people who share similar passions can lead to meaningful connections and friendships.

- **Be open and authentic**: Building supportive relationships requires vulnerability and openness. By being authentic and sharing our thoughts and emotions, we create an environment that encourages others to do the same. Real connections are established on a foundation of mutual respect and comprehension.

- **Practice active listening**: Actively listening to others is a fundamental aspect of creating supportive relationships. Paying attention, showing empathy, and offering validation can strengthen connections and foster a sense of support. By being present in conversations and demonstrating genuine interest, we deepen our understanding of others and build stronger relationships.

- **Offer support to others**: Support is a two-way street. By being there for others in their times of need, we cultivate a culture of reciprocity and strengthen our own support network. Offering a helping hand, providing emotional support, or simply being a good listener can make a significant difference in someone's life and deepen the bond between individuals.

- **Set boundaries**: While it is essential to surround ourselves with supportive individuals, it is equally important to establish healthy boundaries. Recognize when relationships become toxic or draining and prioritize your well-being. Surrounding ourselves with individuals who respect our boundaries and support our growth is crucial for maintaining a positive environment.

Integrate the Strategies Into Your Daily Routine

Maintaining healthy brain health requires incorporating methods into your regular routine. Maintaining the brain's optimal functioning is essential for achieving the best level of cognitive function because it is a complex organ that is always developing. You can make sure that your brain is operating at its best by adding specific habits and actions into your everyday routine. The following advice will assist you in incorporating these practices into your daily life:

Take up a New Hobby

The easiest way to excite your brain is to try something new. This could involve anything from developing a new interest to mastering a musical instrument. The trick is to select a task that actively occupies your brain and necessitates the acquisition of new knowledge or skills. For instance, learning a new language can enhance your memory and cognitive flexibility, while taking up painting or drawing can enable you to improve your spatial reasoning and problem-solving abilities.

Consume a Nutritious Diet to Keep Your Brain Healthy

Making smart food choices can do wonders for your brain health. Opt for nutrient-dense foods such as whole grains, lean proteins, fruits, vegetables, and healthy fats. Likewise, add brain-boosting foods like blueberries, turmeric, broccoli, pumpkin seeds, oranges, and eggs to your daily diet. Remember also to stay well-hydrated. Establish regular meal times and use a meal planner to ensure a balanced and varied diet if necessary.

Continue to Move

Aim to incorporate at least 30 minutes of moderate exercise into your daily routine. This could be anything from a brisk walk during your lunch break, a morning yoga session, or an evening dance class. Make it a point to take breaks from sitting throughout the day by using a standing desk or taking short walks.

Get Adequate Rest

Create a sleep-friendly environment and establish a regular sleep schedule. Aim for at least seven to nine hours of sleep per night. You could establish a relaxing pre-bedtime routine.

Become Social

Engaging in social activities stimulates our brains and keeps us mentally active. Make time each day to connect with others. As such, have a quick phone call to a friend, participate in a club or community event, or even volunteer. Consider virtual interactions through video calls or social media platforms if physical meetings are impossible. Sharing laughter and having meaningful conversations can enrich your mental health significantly.

Keep Your Blood Pressure in Check

Cognitive decline and other detrimental effects of high blood pressure on brain health are possible. Maintaining a healthy weight, exercising, cutting back on drinking, and adopting a nutritious diet are all lifestyle choices that can lower blood pressure and improve brain function.

Control Your Blood Sugar

Maintaining control of your blood sugar is crucial since diabetes raises your risk of developing dementia. By eating healthfully, exercising frequently, and maintaining a healthy weight, diabetes can be prevented. It is crucial to go by your doctor's instructions if you have high blood sugar in order to keep it under control.

Limit Your Alcohol Consumption

Alcohol abuse is a significant risk factor for dementia. By consuming no more than two drinks of alcohol every day, you can reduce the danger.

Keep Your Head Protected

Brain dysfunction is more likely to develop after a head injury. To protect your head and advance healthy brain health, it is crucial to avoid falls, wear a helmet when bicycling or skiing, remove potential hazards from your path, and use proper lighting.

Reduce Stress

To reduce stress, it is essential to incorporate relaxation and stress-reduction strategies into our daily lives. Various techniques, such as yoga, meditation, walking, and listening to music, can promote awareness and relaxation, alleviating the mental and physical effects of stress. Yoga and meditation, with their emphasis on proper breathing and physical postures, help release bodily tension and induce a state of relaxation.

Engaging in physical exercise like walking releases endorphins, which elevate the mood and reduce stress. Listening to music not only has a calming effect on the mind and body but also helps alleviate stress and anxiety.

Finding the right stress reduction method is crucial since different approaches work effectively for different individuals. It is important to incorporate self-care and stress management practices into our daily routines to enhance our overall well-being and mitigate the detrimental effects of stress on our health.

Making wise lifestyle choices as we age plays a significant role in maintaining cognitive abilities and preserving brain sharpness. Setting challenging goals can restructure our brain cells and improve our chances of success.

It has been demonstrated that setting clear, difficult goals improves performance. To accomplish goals and make necessary adjustments along the road, tracking progress is also essential.

By monitoring our progress, we can assess if we are on the right path, identify what is working and what needs to be modified, and adapt our plans accordingly. It is crucial to adopt a brain-friendly lifestyle to promote mental and physical fitness as we age.

Avoiding risk factors such as alcohol consumption, smoking, head trauma, and a sedentary lifestyle can help safeguard the brain from cognitive decline and memory loss.

Regular exercise plays a pivotal role in increasing blood flow and oxygen availability to the brain. This promotes the formation of new brain cells and synapses, contributing to brain health. In addition to physical exercise, maintaining a balanced diet, engaging in mental stimulation, and fostering social connections are all beneficial for the overall health of our brain.

Conclusion

The importance of good nutrition, exercise, and sleep hygiene in preserving a healthy brain has been underlined in this book. We may enhance our memory, cognitive skills, and overall brain function by implementing these techniques into our daily lives, while also lowering our risk of cognitive decline and neurodegenerative disorders. With each chapter presenting useful pointers and suggestions for enhancing brain function, we have kept our promise to provide a thorough manual for enhancing brain health.

A balanced diet is critical for preserving good brain function, as discussed in Chapter 2's part on *Brain Food*. We learned about the nutrients, including antioxidants, B vitamins, and omega-3 fatty acids, which are essential to the well-being of the brain. We also learned that a higher risk of dementia has been linked to diets high in trans and saturated fats, added sweets, and processed foods.

Chapter 3 highlighted the need for exercise for brain health. We discovered that physical activity could improve cognitive performance, emotional stability, and memory. Additionally, we found that exercise can strengthen neural connections through neuroplasticity, enhance sleep quality, and reduce the risk of dementia and cognitive decline.

The emphasis of Chapter 4 was on good sleep practices and how they are essential to preserving normal brain function. We discovered the value of developing a regular sleep schedule, setting up a relaxing sleeping environment, and abstaining from practices like drinking alcohol and using electronics just before bed.

The control and coordination of all physiological functions rests on our immensely intricate brains. For the brain to stay in good shape, a balanced diet, frequent exercise, and excellent sleep are all necessary. In this book, we offer recommendations for enhancing brain health, from the foods we eat to the exercises we do to the sleep we obtain.

The physiology and structure of the brain, the nutrients necessary for brain health, the advantages of physical activity for brain function, and the significance of good sleep hygiene are among the most significant subjects covered in this book. By offering useful tips for preserving sound brain function through a balanced diet, consistent exercise, and adequate sleep, we have fulfilled our pledge.

The science discussed in this book makes it abundantly evident that our lifestyle decisions have a big impact on how well our brains work. The brain is a complicated and important organ that requires a steady supply of nourishment, activity, and restful sleep to function at its best. We can enhance brain function and lower the risk of cognitive decline and neurodegenerative disorders by adopting a balanced diet high in nutrients, exercising frequently, and improving our sleep hygiene.

By talking about the value of diet, exercise, and sleep, we have kept our pledge to offer strategies to improve brain health. Readers can greatly improve their brain health and cognitive performance by putting the advice in this book into practice.

The most important lesson to be learned from this book is that our lifestyle decisions have a big impact on how well our brains work. We may enhance the health of our brains and lower our risk of cognitive decline and neurodegenerative disorders by adopting a balanced diet, exercising frequently, and practicing good sleep hygiene. To guarantee that our brains continue to function at their best throughout our lives, it is crucial to place a high priority on brain health and take good care of our bodies.

The importance of good nutrition, exercise, and sleep hygiene in preserving a healthy brain has been underlined in this book. We may enhance our memory, cognitive skills, and overall brain function by implementing these techniques into our daily lives, while also lowering our risk of cognitive decline and neurodegenerative disorders. With each chapter presenting useful pointers and suggestions for enhancing brain function, we have kept our promise to provide a thorough manual for enhancing brain health.

We want you to learn the importance of prioritizing your brain health as the key lesson from this book. Taking care of our brains is absolutely essential for living a healthy and full life since they are the center of everything we do, think, and feel. We can take efforts to maximize our brain health and raise our general well-being by paying attention to the useful advice provided in this book.

Glossary

Antioxidants: Substances that protect cells from damage caused by free radicals.

B vitamins: A group of water-soluble vitamins that are important for brain function and other bodily processes.

Blood pressure: The pressure exerted by blood against the arterial walls, influenced by various factors such as diet, exercise, stress, and medication.

Brain development: The growth and transformation of the brain, particularly during childhood, as it adapts to new experiences and forms neural connections.

Brain function: The ability of the brain to process and respond to stimuli.

Brain optimization: The process of enhancing brain function through various techniques and strategies, such as exercise, diet, cognitive training, and meditation.

Cell membranes: Thin layers made up of lipids, proteins, and carbohydrates that surround and protect the cell, control the flow of molecules in and out of the cell, and communicate with other cells to maintain tissue and organ function.

Chronic diseases: Conditions that persist for an extended period, typically lasting more than three months, and require ongoing management and treatment. Examples include heart disease, stroke, cancer, diabetes, obesity, and Alzheimer's.

Circadian rhythms: Sleep-wake cycles, hormone secretion, and metabolism are all governed by natural 24-hour cycles. These rhythms are regulated by the internal biological clock, which responds to external cues such as light and temperature.

Cognitive belief system: A theoretical framework that describes how individuals actively process information and construct their own belief systems, attitudes, and values. These cognitive structures shape how individuals perceive and interpret the world around them.

Cognitive decline: The gradual deterioration of cognitive function, such as memory, attention, and problem-solving, that is commonly associated with aging. This decline can also be caused by neurological conditions or brain injuries.

Cognitive function: Learning, perception, memory, attention, and problem-solving are all mental activities. These functions rely on the complex interactions between neurons and brain structures.

Cognitive skills: The mental abilities and processes that enable individuals to acquire, process, and use information effectively. These skills include perception, attention, memory, language, and reasoning, and are essential for success in education, work, and daily life.

Concentration: The ability to direct and maintain attention towards a specific task or stimulus while ignoring distractions. Concentration is essential for learning, problem-solving, and task completion.

Connections: Synaptic connections are the points of contact between neurons where signals are transmitted through the release of neurotransmitters. These connections are crucial for communication between neurons and the transmission of nerve impulses, allowing for the integration of information and the coordination of complex behaviors.

Context-Dependent Memory: The phenomenon where memory recall is enhanced when the environmental context at the time of retrieval matches the context in which the information was learned or encoded. Contextual cues can help trigger memories and improve retrieval.

Declarative Memory: A sort of long-term memory that relates to memories that may be expressed and discussed verbally. Declarative memory is separated into two types: semantic memory (generic knowledge) and episodic memory (personal experiences).

Dementia: A neurological disorder that results in a decline in cognitive function and interferes with daily activities. Symptoms include memory loss, impaired language, reduced judgment, and changes in behavior and mood. Alzheimer's disease is the most frequent kind of dementia.

Endorphins: A type of neurotransmitter produced by the central nervous system that interacts with specific receptors in the brain to reduce pain and promote feelings of pleasure and well-being. Endorphins are released during exercise, eating, and other pleasurable activities.

Energy Metabolism: The biochemical process by which the body converts food into energy (ATP) that can be used by cells to perform work. Energy metabolism involves the breakdown of carbohydrates, fats, and proteins, which are then processed through the Krebs cycle and oxidative phosphorylation.

Executive Function: A series of cognitive processes that enable people to control their behavior and complete complex activities. Executive function includes skills such as planning, organizing, initiating, inhibiting, shifting, and monitoring actions, and is essential for goal-directed behavior and adaptation to changing circumstances.

Exercise: Physical exercise undertaken to improve fitness, health, or general well-being. Exercise can take many forms, including aerobic activity, strength training, and flexibility exercises, and has numerous health benefits, including reducing the risk of chronic diseases, improving mood, and enhancing cognitive function.

Frontal Lobe: The biggest lobe of the brain, responsible for higher cognitive activities such as planning, decision making, and personality. It also controls voluntary movement, speech production, and other complex motor functions.

Glial cells: The nervous system's non-neuronal cells support neurons structurally and are essential to the nervous system's proper operation. Glial cells include astrocytes, oligodendrocytes, and microglia.

Growth Factors: A group of signaling molecules that promote neuronal development, survival, and repair. For the brain to develop and operate properly, growth factors such as neurotrophins, cytokines, and hormones are essential.

Hippocampus: A brain region with a seahorse form that is linked to memory and learning. It plays a significant role in memory development and retrieval and is an essential component of the limbic system.

Information Processing Model: A theoretical framework outlining the information storage and processing mechanisms of the brain. The model proposes that information is first encoded through attention and perception, then processed through short-term memory and working memory, and finally consolidated into long-term memory.

Information processing: The capacity of the brain to take in, analyze, and store data. It involves a complex network of neural circuits that enable the brain to process sensory information, make decisions, and form memories.

Lifestyle decisions: Choices related to diet, exercise, sleep, and other behaviors that can impact health.

Memory consolidation: The process of converting short-term memories into long-term memories through a series of biochemical and neural changes in the brain, including the strengthening of synapses and the reorganization of neural networks.

Mental engagement: Activities that encourage cognitive stimulation and growth by putting cognitive processes, such as problem-solving, critical analysis, and creative analysis, to use.

Mood regulation: The process by which the body regulates emotions, such as happiness, sadness, anger, and anxiety, through a complex interplay of biological, psychological, and social factors.

Mood: The emotional state or general emotional tone of an individual, which can be influenced by a number of elements, such as genetics, environment, and life events.

Natural vegetation: Plants and other greenery that grow without human intervention, often in natural environments such as forests, fields, or parks. The creation of oxygen, the storage of carbon, and soil preservation are just a few of the crucial functions that these ecosystems offer.

Neurodegenerative Disorders: Alzheimer's disease, Parkinson's disease, and Huntington's disease are among a group of illnesses that are defined by the gradual loss of nerve cells and mental capacity.

Neuroplasticity: The brain's ability to alter and adapt in response to experiences by creating new brain cells and strengthening neural connections. This procedure is essential for memory retention, learning, and brain injury rehabilitation.

Nourishment: The process of providing the body with nutrients through food and drink.

Omega-3 fatty acids: Essential fatty acids that are important for brain and heart health.

Perception: A method by which the brain groups and analyzes sensory data from the environment to produce a subjective perception of the world. This process involves not only the sensory organs, but also the brain's interpretation of the sensory input.

Physical activity: Any form of movement that requires energy expenditure.

Pillars of brain optimization: The five main areas of focus for maintaining and improving brain health and function: proper nutrition, physical activity, sleep, social connections, and mental engagement. These pillars work in conjunction with each other to promote overall brain health, and each one is essential to maintaining optimal cognitive function.

Prioritizing: Making something a top priority or giving it special attention and importance.

Psychophysical connection: The relationship between the mind and the physical environment, particularly how sensory input affects cognitive and emotional processes. This connection highlights how external stimuli can impact our internal processes, and vice versa.

Restricting beliefs: Negative or limiting beliefs that can impede personal growth and development. These beliefs may be internalized from past experiences, cultural norms, or social conditioning, and can significantly impact a person's self-perception and potential.

Retrieval Cues: Environmental or contextual stimuli that serve as reminders and can trigger the retrieval of information stored in memory. These cues can be anything from sights, sounds, or smells to emotional or situational triggers.

Retrieval: The action of getting information from memory after it has been encoded and saved. Retrieval can occur spontaneously, or it can be prompted by specific retrieval cues or intentional efforts to access the information.

Self-care: The practice of taking care of one's physical, emotional, and mental health, especially through activities such as exercise, healthy eating, and stress management. It involves setting aside time for oneself to prioritize personal well-being and prevent burnout.

Sense of purpose: A feeling of having a clear and meaningful reason for living and taking action. It is a fundamental human need that drives motivation and helps individuals find direction and fulfillment in life.

Sleep hygiene: Behaviors and practices that promote healthy sleep, such as maintaining a consistent sleep schedule, creating a comfortable sleeping environment, avoiding stimulants before bedtime, and limiting screen time.

Slumber: The state of sleep and its impact on brain function, including memory consolidation, emotional regulation, and physical restoration. It is fundamental to one's general health and well-being.

Social connection: The experience of feeling close and connected to others, including family, friends, and community members. Social connections are important for mental health, social support, and overall life satisfaction.

Social engagement: The act of interacting with others in a meaningful way, often with the goal of building relationships, promoting well-being, and participating in activities.

Social institutions: A system of social relationships and organizations that support and facilitate a society's functions.

Social welfare: Programs designed to provide financial, educational, medical, and other assistance to individuals and families who are in need.

Stimulants: Substances that increase alertness and energy, such as caffeine and nicotine.

Strength training: Physical activity that involves resistance, such as weightlifting, to increase muscle strength and endurance.

Stress management: Methods and strategies to lower stress and encourage relaxation, such as mindfulness, meditation, exercise, and adequate sleep.

Synapse: The connection between two nerve cells that allows for communication between them.

Tai Chi: A kind of Chinese martial art that incorporates calm, flowing motions and meditation. Both its health advantages and its self-defense tactics are used in its practice. Balance, flexibility, strength, and general physical and mental health have all been demonstrated to improve with Tai Chi.

Therapy: A form of treatment for mental or emotional disorders that involves talking with a trained professional to gain insight, resolve problems, and develop coping strategies. There are numerous ways that treatment can be delivered, including cognitive-behavioral therapy, psychoanalytic therapy, and group therapy.

Tranquil sleeping environment: An atmosphere that is peaceful, quiet, cool, and cozy while sleeping. In order to achieve the best sleep quality and duration, it is crucial to create a tranquil and peaceful environment. This can involve eliminating noise and distractions, adjusting the temperature of the room to a comfortable level, and using blackout curtains or eye masks to block out light.

Trans and saturated fats: Types of fats that can increase the risk of heart disease and other health problems.

Walking in nature: A natural setting, such as a forest, park, or wilderness area, where walking or hiking is practiced. Walking in nature has been found to have many positive effects on mental and physical health, such as reducing stress and anxiety, boosting mood, and improving cardiovascular health.

Well-being: Refers to one's general condition of health and happiness, which includes emotional, mental, and physical well-being. Well-being is a subjective concept that varies across individuals and cultures and is influenced by many factors, including social, economic, and environmental factors.

Working Memory: Refers to the cognitive function responsible for holding and manipulating information temporarily in the brain. Working memory is crucial for a range of cognitive tasks, including problem-solving, decision-making, and language comprehension. Although short-term memory and it are frequently used interchangeably, they are two distinct cognitive processes. Short-term memory can store information for only a few seconds while working memory can store information for a few seconds to minutes.

References

Brain Structure and Function. (2017). Northern Brain Injury Association British Columbia. https://www.nbia.ca/brain-structure-function/

Carlson, N. R. (2014). *Physiology of Behavior*. Pearson.

Carlson, N. R. (2021). *Physiology of Behavior (13th ed.)*. Pearson.

Carpinello, S. E., & Haskins, R. (2021). *Mental health and Well-Being: Contemporary Issues and Future Directions*. Routledge.

Goldstein, E. B. (2020). *Cognitive Psychology: Connecting Mind, Research, and Everyday Experience*. Cengage Learning.

Help Your Brain Stay Sharp. (2021). Centers for Disease Control and Prevention. https://www.cdc.gov/nccdphp/dnpao/features/physical-activity-brain-health/index.html

James, G. (n.d.). *What goal setting does to your brain. IncAfrica*. https://incafrica.com/library/geoffrey-james-what-goal-setting-does-to-your-brain-why-its-spectacularly-effective

Johnson, A. B., & Smith, B. C. (2020). *Brain Anatomy and Function*. Oxford University Press.

Keltner, D., & Marsh, J. (2018). *The Compassionate Instinct: The Science of Human Goodness*. WW Norton & Company.

Kryger, M. H., Roth, T., & Dement, W. C. (2017). *Principles and Practice of Sleep Medicine (6th ed.)*. Elsevier.

Martin, G. N., & Carlson, N. R. (2019). *Psychology*. Pearson.

McEwen, B. S., & Lasley, E. N. (2002). *The End of Stress As We Know It*. Joseph Henry Press.

Medina, J. (2014). *Brain Rules: 12 Principles for Surviving and Thriving at Work, Home, and School*. Pear Press.

Myers, D. G. (2014). *Exploring Psychology*. Worth Publishers.

Robinson, L., Smith, M., & Segal, R. (2019). *Stress Management*. Help Guide. https://www.helpguide.org/articles/stress/stress-management.htm

Sternberg, R. J. (2019). *Cognitive Psychology (7th ed.)*. Cengage Learning.

10 Ways to Improve Brain Health. (2019). TenetHealth. https://www.tenethealth.com/healthy-living/corporate-content/10-ways-to-improve-brain-health

Yale School of Medicine: Sleep's Crucial Role in Preserving Memory. (2022). Wham Now. https://whamnow.org/news/yale-school-of-medicine-sleeps-crucial-role-in-preserving-memory/